HOW EVERYDAY THINGS WORK

60 Descriptions and Activities

Peter Goodwin

illustrated by Nicholas Soloway

J. Weston Walch, Publisher
Portland, Maine

Users' Guide
to
Walch Reproducible Books

As part of our general effort to provide educational materials which are as practical and economical as possible, we have designated this publication a "reproducible book." The designation means that purchase of the book includes purchase of the right to limited reproduction of all pages on which this symbol appears:

Here is the basic Walch policy: We grant to individual purchasers of this book the right to make sufficient copies of reproducible pages for use by all students of a single teacher. This permission is limited to a single teacher, and does not apply to entire schools or school systems, so institutions purchasing the book should pass the permission on to a single teacher. Copying of the book or its parts for resale is prohibited.

Any questions regarding this policy or requests to purchase further reproduction rights should be addressed to:

Permissions Editor
J. Weston Walch, Publisher
P.O. Box 658
Portland, ME 04104-0658

—*J. Weston Walch, Publisher*

1   2   3   4   5   6   7   8   9   10

ISBN 0-8251-1974-X

Contents

NOTE: An **(E)** indicates that the unit involves an experiment.

Sound and Light

Thermodynamics

Environmental Science

Introduction

This book is dedicated to the idea that if students can see science around them, they will become more interested in learning about it. Often, their schooling seems separate from their day-to-day lives. This book helps students to see how things work. Through knowledge of applications, they take their learning out of the classroom and ultimately learn more.

The application of scientific principles to everyday objects, systems, and events is what this book is all about. Using little or no math, each unit contains a student section and a teacher section. The student section is self-contained, although students should be familiar with the general ideas involved before they read the unit. Specifics are covered in the unit. Some of the units involve activities, either for pairs or for larger groups of students. These activities are simple experiments that allow students to learn some science, use the scientific method, see how things work, and have fun.

These units will allow students to take scientific principles out of the classroom. They can be done as assignments or as in-class exercises. The questions at the end of the sections can be used for homework or to direct class discussions. The topics should help students see the value of their studies.

—Peter Goodwin

How to Use This Book

Each unit consists of a student section and a teacher section. The student section presents the descriptions. In the experiment-oriented units, a topic is developed and then the students are directed in their investigation. In the other units, an idea is developed and then questions can be used either for homework problems or as the start of a class discussion. The teacher section includes answers to questions, a more complete discussion of the scientific ideas, and background information.

For ease of copying, the student sections generally consist of one page for experiments and two pages for non-experiments. With an understanding of the basic ideas covered, students can comprehend these sections without much preparation. For example, in the unit on switches, students should understand that current flows in wires in a circuit and that a battery makes the current flow and can illuminate a light. Because only general ideas are presupposed, the units can be used early on in the discussion of particular topics. When possible, teachers should use demonstrations to reinforce the ideas presented.

The experiments have been designed to use simple, inexpensive materials. This should make most of these experiments possible even under an austere budget.

1

How Is a Floor Like a Bridge?

Most floors are like bridges in that they support an expanse between two uprights. A floor must be able to carry the weight of things placed on it—people, furniture, etc. If the floor can't support the weight, it may collapse. But how are floors built and what is required to make a floor sturdy?

What things must be taken into account as you build a floor? As you might imagine, the greater the distance between supports, the stronger the floor must be. The floor is made stronger by using larger pieces of wood, or perhaps by using steel instead of wood. But what is the most efficient way to support the weight placed on the floor?

Conduct an experiment to find the best way to place boards. Use a meterstick and two blocks of wood. Place the supports about .3 m (1 ft) apart. Then

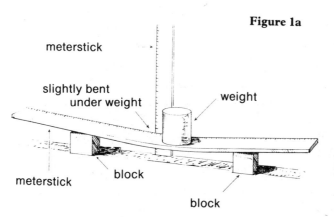

Figure 1a

meterstick

slightly bent under weight

weight

meterstick

block

block

place the meterstick across the blocks, with the wide edge down, as shown in Figure 1a. Now, place a weight on the "board" and see how much the board bends. Repeat your experiment, but place the meterstick with its narrow edge down. Record your observations. Be careful not to exert too much force or you may break the meterstick.

Now, move the supports twice as far apart. Repeat your experiments and record your observations. What happens when the supports are farther apart? What could you do to make the board bend less? What do you suppose people who design floors do when they want to increase the distance between supports for a floor?

TEACHER

Materials Needed		
two metersticks	two blocks of wood	one weight

Building floors is a necessary part of all construction. With housing construction, most floors are built out of wood, usually 2 × 8's, in the United States. When the rooms are larger, there are two ways in which architects can build the floor: they can use larger lumber, 2 × 10's, or put supports under the middle of the room.

The experiment in this section is quite easy to set up and uses minimal equipment. Students quickly see how the placement of the board reduces the bending. It allows a larger span. When the meterstick is on its large, flat side, weights bend it easily. When it is on edge, it holds much more.

You can use metersticks or other wooden sticks, but it is helpful if the wood stands on its edge as a meterstick does. The weights should be .5 kg (1 lb) or less, or you may break your meterstick. You should encourage students to record their observations and note the amount of bending and separation distance as precisely as possible. You may want to have the students use a variety of weights and collect data relating to how much bending occurs with twice the weight, etc.

You can extend this exercise by having students use toothpicks and glue to build bridges across a certain span. You can then have a competition to see which structure can take the most weight before it breaks.

When weight is put on the board, the board wants to bend. To prevent bending, the top of the board resists compression while the bottom of the board is being pulled apart, as shown in Figure 1b. The middle of

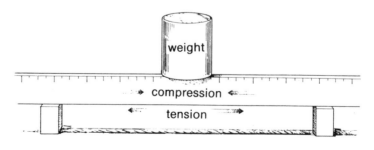

Figure 1b

the board does little other than separate the top and bottom. This is why I beams are used. An I beam gets rid of most of this "middle" and reduces the weight of the beam. The farther apart the top and the bottom, the stronger it is. This is true of boards, too. A board is stronger when on edge than on its side.

2
How a Rocket Works in Space

If you are standing on an ice rink and someone pushes you, you move one way and the person moves the other way. This is a demonstration of one of Newton's laws. For every force, there is an equal and opposite force. But how does a rocket move in outer space? What does the rocket push on?

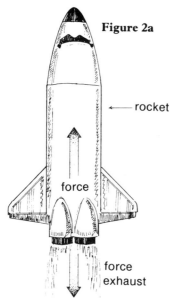

Figure 2a

rocket

force

force
exhaust

Newton's Law can't be broken. Rockets move because they push fuel out of the back of the rocket, as shown in Figure 2a. When fuel is burned, it expands and is pushed out the rear of the rocket. The force the rocket exerts on the fuel equals the force the fuel exerts on the rocket. Fuel moves backward and the rocket moves forward.

The fuel is pushed out as rapidly as possible because the faster it moves away from the rocket, the faster the rocket moves forward. The size of the force is related to the mass of the fuel and the speed at which the mass moves out the back. Not much fuel goes out the back of the rocket in a given moment, but it moves very quickly. This exerts a sizable force on the rocket.

Figure 2b

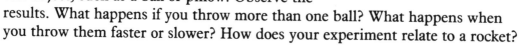

velocity

basketball

backward

motion

skateboard

It is possible to model how rockets work by standing on a platform that can move opposed by little friction and by throwing objects away from you. A skateboard moves with relatively little friction. If you stand on a skateboard and throw an object one way, you move the other way, as shown in Figure 2b. On a smooth surface where you can work safely, throw a soft object, such as a ball or pillow. Observe the results. What happens if you throw more than one ball? What happens when you throw them faster or slower? How does your experiment relate to a rocket?

Remember, your "rocket" is moving on the earth and friction tends to stop it. In space, there is almost no frictional force on the rocket, so it does not slow down like the skateboard.

How Everyday Things Work

TEACHER

Materials Needed

one or more skateboards   a piece of plywood

safety equipment   four C clamps

large, light objects (basketballs or pillows)

This experiment needs to be done in a proper place. All students who participate must wear helmets and all necessary safety equipment. Students must be able to work without bumping into objects or causing damage. The surface must be smooth and thrown objects must be soft. Large, light objects—like basketballs—work well and pose little risk to spectators.

Ask each of two students to bring in a skateboard for the day's event; those students can then be the "rocket." Owners of the skateboards should have better balance on the board and won't fall off when throwing the objects. A movable platform may be made using C clamps, a piece

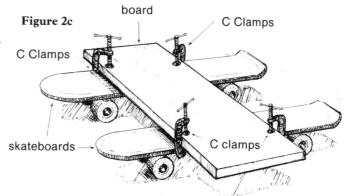

Figure 2c board C Clamps C Clamps skateboards → C clamps

of plywood that will cover two skateboards, and two skateboards, as shown in Figure 2c.

Make sure that the student throws a varied number of objects at different speeds to test the results of these changes. If balls are thrown at the same speed, throwing two balls should give the person on the skateboard twice the velocity. Given the same number of balls thrown, the ones thrown faster should cause a greater change in the speed.

The actual equation for the motion demonstrated in this experiment is:

$$p = m_{weight}v_{weight} = m_{person}v_{person}$$

where p is momentum, m is mass, and v is velocity. Because the objects that are thrown have much less mass than the person throwing them, the person moves at less velocity than the objects.

Rockets are limited in the rate at which they can accelerate by how quickly the gas molecules of the exhaust leave the rocket. Gas molecules at high temperature move faster than cooler molecules, so the aim of rocket builders is to have high-temperature gases. The challenge here is to avoid melting the nozzles that emit the gases. The amount of mass that can be sent backwards (the fuel) is limited by the total amount of upward force the rocket can produce. If the upward force is less than the weight of the rocket, the rocket doesn't leave the launch pad until it uses some fuel. The old *Apollo* spacecrafts took off very slowly from the launch pad. They were so heavy that the upward thrust nearly equalled the weight. As fuel was burned, the acceleration became greater because the weight of the rocket decreased. This is why rockets are often built in stages. After one section is used, it is discarded to reduce the mass of the spacecraft as much as possible. With less mass, the acceleration is greater.

3

Air Friction and Riding a Bicycle

Racing bicycles have handlebars that make you lean over them. Why are they made this way? What are the advantages?

When you ride a bicycle fast, much of the energy you put into the pedals goes to air friction. If you are going at 20 mph (10 m/sec), about 90% of the energy is lost to air friction. The rest goes to the tires and to the pedals. If you lean over the handlebars and become more "streamlined," you reduce air friction.

Figure 3

Experimenting with air friction and bicycles is only easy if you have a long hill. You can start at the top of a hill and coast down a measured distance, timing how long it takes. By dividing the distance by time, you can determine your average velocity. You can then change the amount of air friction by leaning over the handlebars and seeing what happens to the velocity.

The problem with this experiment is that the difference in air friction between sitting straight up and leaning over the handlebars is not very great. You need a high velocity to get good results. An easier experiment uses wads of paper. Take a piece of paper and wad it up into a ball. Stand on a chair and drop the paper. Time how long it takes to hit the floor. Then make the wad looser. How long does it take now?

As you do your timing, you must try to avoid errors due to reaction time. Timing errors occur as you stop or start the stopwatch. Generally, a timer can anticipate when an object will hit and will stop the watch at that moment. Starting the watch at the moment the object is dropped is harder unless you can anticipate the moment it is dropped. This can be done if the timer drops the object or the person dropping it says, "One, two, three, drop."

As you experiment, try to see what things affect the rate at which the wad falls. Sometimes it will fall at an unpredicted rate. Can you explain why?

TEACHER

Materials Needed
paper   stopwatch

This experiment does not produce very precise results. Students will be able to get an idea as to what factors affect air friction, but because the wads of paper are not of uniform shape, the data may not be repeatable.

The differences in times for the falls are related to air friction. The force is actually related to the square or the cube of the velocity. If you are going twice as fast, the force on you is at least four times greater ($2^2 = 4$), if not eight times greater ($2^3 = 8$). At three times the speed, there is nine times the force ($3^2 = 9$). The force increases as the square of velocity for relatively streamlined flow. It is a cube when the air does not flow past it in a streamlined fashion.

You may want to have a competition for the fastest and slowest falling wads of paper. The problem is starting them at the same time to see which one falls faster. If you use a board to hold the wads in the air and then quickly remove the board, the wads will fall together. You must be careful not to make too much air move downward so as to draw some wads downward faster than the others.

It is relatively easy to see which hits first and last. If you are working on the slowest falling wad, you may want to make a rule about where the wad lands. If the paper is built like an airplane, it may stay in the air a long time but will not fall to the ground in the "correct" manner. A square measuring one meter on a side is a good target, but you can try other shaped spaces as well.

4

How You Make a Swing Go Higher

A swing is an interesting example of physics. It moves like a pendulum in a clock, but a swing is interesting in that *you* can "pump" and make yourself go higher. How do you actually make yourself go higher? What steps do you take?

A physicist would say that pumping gives energy to you and to the swing. When you are moving on a swing, you obviously have energy because if you hit someone or something in the path of your swing, it hurts. When you pump with your legs, you actually lift yourself up. The lifting makes you swing higher because you drop a bit farther down with each swing.

As you pump, you raise yourself upwards in two ways. First, you raise your feet above where they are normally when you sit. Raising your feet and legs raises your center of mass. Second, you bend the ropes of the swing as you raise your legs. This makes the seat and your body move upwards. Both of these actions raise mass, which then falls after you reach the high point, as shown in Figure 4a.

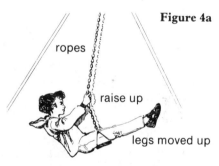

Figure 4a

ropes

raise up

legs moved up

raised center of mass

When you swing, you must pump at the right time or you don't go higher. You time your pumping so that you raise mass when the swing is at its lowest point. The ropes exert the upward force needed to pull you up and you don't change your motion. Then, when you are at the highest point, you lower the mass. Whenever anything falls, it moves faster. Because you lower your mass at the highest point, you fall the distance you raised your body plus the distance you swung up, as shown in Figure 4b. You fall farther than you swung up. By falling farther each time you swing, you go higher. If you are not swinging at all on the swing, pumping doesn't work. When you raise or lower your mass, you move up and down.

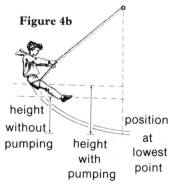

Figure 4b

height without pumping

height with pumping

position at lowest point

Use a swing and see if this explanation agrees with how you make a swing go higher. Can you see other things that help raise your center of mass? How far do you raise your center of mass when you bend the ropes? Be careful never to walk in the path of someone who is swinging.

TEACHER

Swinging is something that most students have done but have never really understood. This section explains how pumping a swing makes it go higher. It is not a complete analysis of the problem, but it is a starting point.

The reason this is not a complete analysis is that some work is also done on the backswing so that energy is added to the swing both going forward and backward. The net effect of pumping in each direction is the same, however. In some way, mass is raised and it falls farther on each swing than it swung up. If you swing without pumping, you swing lower and lower because friction takes energy from the system.

The timing of the pumping is important. If you raise your center of mass when you are going up, then you slow down as you do it. The amount of kinetic energy, or energy of motion, which you had at the lowest point goes to making you go higher. Raising your center of mass at the bottom adds energy more quickly. When you raise yourself at this position, you pull on ropes that are vertical. The ropes pull on you and you move straight up. The distance you move up gives you a little more potential energy, which is added to the kinetic energy you had at the lowest point. Therefore, when you come down the next time, you fall from a higher position. The energy to make you go higher comes from the work your arms do on the ropes and your legs do when you raise them.

When you go outside to see how people swing, you should have the students do a few things. First, you should have them sit on swings and not move. Then have them lean back and put their feet out. They should observe that the seats of the swings rise. This gives the person more potential energy to be released. When the person returns to the sitting position, however, he or she doesn't swing higher because all the motion is up and down. Students can see how the center of mass moves more clearly on a stationary swing.

Next, the students can observe the motion when someone is swinging. They should particularly note what happens when the person on the swing moves in a particular way. It is easier to see this when the person is just getting started.

Have the different groups write a description in their own words of how someone pumps a swing. This helps them to clarify their analyses. Whenever they go swinging in the future, they will think back to the physics that govern their motion.

5

How a String Trimmer
Cuts Through Weeds

A popular home gardening tool, the string trimmer, takes advantage of some nice physics to do its job. It is basically a simple device. It makes a small string, generally made of plastic, move rapidly in circles. When the rapidly moving string hits an object, it exerts a force on it, as shown in Figure 5. That force is often enough to break the stem of a plant.

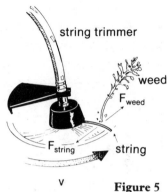

Figure 5

The reason the string trimmer can trim weeds and grass is that the string is moving fast. One of Sir Isaac Newton's laws says, "An object in motion tends to stay in motion unless acted on by an unbalanced force." The faster the object is moving, the more force it takes to stop it. You worry more about being hit by a fastball than by one that is tossed gently to you.

If you have used a trimmer, you may have noticed that when the string gets too short it doesn't work well. The string moves in a small circle. Because it travels around a smaller circumference, it goes a shorter distance each time it goes around, and it travels slower. When it moves slower, it exerts less force when it is stopped. On the other hand, if the string gets too long, air friction becomes greater. The trimmer can't keep the string moving fast enough and the weeds don't get cut.

Two things may prevent the trimmer from cutting a weed. First, the weed may be too strong and the force of the string is not enough to break it. Second, the weed may move too easily and the string doesn't change its motion enough to exert a large force.

You can model a weed trimmer by swinging a rope in a circle. **Be careful not to hit anyone as you do this.** Take a rope and swing a half-foot section around in a circle. You probably can't get it going fast enough to hurt anything. Now, swing a 1-meter section. The end of the rope is now going six times faster. Try hitting the ground and think about whether you would like to be hit with this section. If you have weeds around you, try it on some weeds. Now, try swinging a 3-meter section of rope. What happens? Is this as effective as the 1-meter section?

How Everyday Things Work

TEACHER

Materials Needed
a length of rope

WARNING: This experiment needs to be well supervised because swinging ropes can injure other students. It is best to have only one rope for the entire class.

The students experiment with the two variables of the string trimmer. They should find that they must swing the rope as fast as possible, but the length is also critical to the trimmer's effectiveness. If it is too short, it does little cutting of weeds. If it is too long, they cannot swing it fast enough because of air friction. Air friction works on the entire length of the rope, so the frictional forces increase rapidly with a longer rope. This is why you keep adjusting the string in the trimmer to a particular length.

The force from the string accelerates the portion of the weed or grass it hits. When the trimmer cuts the weed, a section of the weed or grass is broken away from the rest of the weed by this acceleration.

In order to exert a large force, the string must be going at a very high rate of speed. The equation to find the force is given as:

$$\text{force} = \frac{(\text{mass})(\text{change in velocity})}{(\text{change in time})}$$

A larger mass and a larger change in velocity (the string slows down as it hits the weed) both cause a larger force. A smaller change in time or a more abrupt stop cause a larger force. When you stop quickly in a car, there is more force on you. A similar thing happens when the string slows down rapidly.

6
Why Doors and Other Things Squeak

Figure 6a

Two very unpleasant noises have the same cause. Something sticks and slips and then sticks and slips again and again. This is known as the *stick-slip* process. When you move your fingernails along the chalkboard, the nail sticks because of friction. As you move your hand, more and more force tries to make the nail move. Eventually the nail slides. The distance the nail moves before it stops again is very small. The moving hand causes the nail to move again as more force is exerted on the nail. The resulting noise can send shivers up some people's spines just thinking about it.

The nail sticking and slipping happens very rapidly. The frequency at which this happens is related to the rate at which the nail vibrates back and forth. It vibrates at a high frequency so you hear a high-pitched squeak.

A door squeaks for the same reason. Some part of the door hinge sticks and then releases its grip only to stick again. The noise occurs because every time the hinge starts to move, it breaks bonds that release energy in the form of sound. Oiling the hinge prevents both the sticking and the noise.

Figure 6b

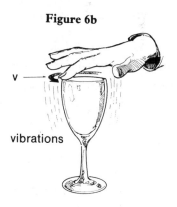

A pleasant example of stick-slip noises is the way a wineglass will "sing." Moisten your finger and run it around the edge of a glass, as shown in Figure 6b. The glass makes a note characteristic of the glass and the amount of fluid it is holding. As you move your finger around the glass, it periodically sticks and then slips. The wineglass itself starts vibrating. The vibration in the glass helps cause the finger to slip at particular times.

Run an experiment with a wineglass to see what factors affect the pitch that is produced. Any stemmed glass will "sing" with a little trial and error. Try to figure out what amount of water on your finger and the rim of the glass works best. Test to see how different amounts of water in the glass affect the pitch. Try to play a scale or a tune with a number of glasses.

How Everyday Things Work

TEACHER

This experiment can be done quite easily with inexpensive wineglasses. Often you can find them in a discount store for a dollar or so. The only requirement is that they have stems. This allows you to hold the bottom of the glass and rub the top. Because the top is supported by just one point, the bowl is free to vibrate. Even cheap glasses should sing. Regular glasses don't sing because when you hold them by the side, you take away the energy that causes the vibration in the glass.

Students should find that if the finger is too wet or too dry, there is no sound. When the finger is too wet, the finger won't stick. When it is too dry, the finger sticks and slips at irregular time intervals. This does not produce a tone. With the right degree of wetness, the bowl of the glass starts to vibrate at one of its "natural" frequencies. The vibration helps cause the slipping, so once the glass starts to sing, it is easier to keep it singing.

The frequency at which a wineglass vibrates is related to the stiffness of the glass and to the mass that must be vibrated. With stiffer glass, the vibrations are faster so the pitch is higher. With more mass, either with more water or with leaded glass, the frequency of vibration decreases and you hear a lower pitch. If students put water in the glasses, they may be able to play tunes. With care, you can have them make a scale and then rub the glasses at the correct times.

The squeaky door and the nails on the chalkboard work in much the same way as the wineglass. The nails vibrate at such a high pitch because the nails are rather stiff while having a small amount of mass. This makes for a very high vibration rate. This noise can be eliminated if the fingers are placed at a different angle. Another example of the stick-slip process is a violin. As the bow is drawn across the strings, it sticks and then slips. Once the string starts to vibrate, the bow starts to stick and slip at that rate.

Many objects vibrate at characteristic frequencies. If you hold a meterstick off the edge of a table and "snap" the free end, it will vibrate at its characteristic frequency. If you change the amount of the meterstick that is off the edge of the table, you will get a different frequency. The wineglass vibrates at a characteristic frequency, as well.

7

Why Tides Occur

Tides are amazing. Huge amounts of water are moved in and out of bays. In the Bay of Fundy in Canada, water levels change as much as 15 meters (45 ft) between high and low tide. What causes these huge tidal flows?

One way to show why tides occur uses *differential gravitational force*. The gravitational force between two objects is determined by how far apart they are. The farther apart, the weaker the force. The distance from the center of the earth to the moon is about 60 times the earth's radius. Therefore, the side of the earth that faces the moon is about 59 times the length of the earth's radius away from the moon. The side that faces away from the moon has a distance from the moon of 61 times the earth's radius, as shown in Figure 7a.

Figure 7a

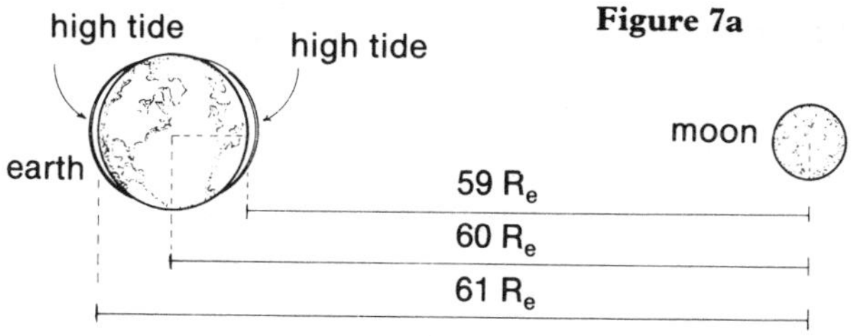

high tide

high tide

earth

moon

$59 R_e$

$60 R_e$

$61 R_e$

The difference in distance is important because gravitational force is weaker when objects are farther away. If we calculate the gravitational force exerted by the moon on a kilogram at the center of the earth, it is a little smaller than the force on a kilogram on the side facing the moon. Likewise, the force at the center is a little larger than the force on a kilogram on the side away from the moon.

This difference in force on a kilogram in different places is a "differential" force. Water on the side of the earth facing the moon is pulled away from the earth. The earth acts as a solid sphere, and the water is pulled slightly up from the surface causing a high tide. But there are two high tides a day! The other tide is caused because the earth is literally pulled away from the water on the side away from the moon. High tides occur on the sides of the earth that face and are away from the moon.

The tides described above would occur on a globe that had no solid ground. Because of the solid ground on the earth (the continents and islands), things are a little different. Because it takes a while for the water to slosh around land masses, high tides can occur at quite different times only a few miles apart. For example, the time for high tide may be different in Boston than in Cape Cod. Even though these places are not far away from each other and they are both pointed toward the moon at the same time, it takes more time for the water to move in and out of Boston Harbor. A canal cuts across the west end of Cape Cod. It is only a few miles long, but the high tide on the north side is a few hours different from high tide on the south side. Water literally flows back and forth through the canal because one side is higher than the other. The current can actually be quite strong and small boats may not be able to make progress against the current.

Figure 7c

moon

Figure 7b

earth

sun

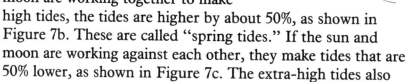

moon

earth

sun

The sun also affects tides, but the effects are much smaller because even though the sun has a large mass, it is much farther away than the moon. It causes tides that are about half as big as the moon's. The sun's effect does make a difference in the height of the tides. If the sun and the moon are working together to make high tides, the tides are higher by about 50%, as shown in Figure 7b. These are called "spring tides." If the sun and moon are working against each other, they make tides that are 50% lower, as shown in Figure 7c. The extra-high tides also cause extra-low tides, so if you want to get to a clam bed that is normally under water, you might wait for a spring tide. The water goes a long way out and you can get the clams that normally can't be dug. It is a problem if spring tides occur when a storm approaches. The storm can make the already high tides higher and cause flooding.

Review Questions

1) What is a "differential force" and how is it caused by the moon?

2) What happens to the water on the earth to produce two high tides a day?

3) Why aren't the high tides at two places near each other always at the same time?

4) What effect does the sun have on tides? What benefits can it bring, what dangers?

TEACHER

Answers

1) A "differential force" is a force that exerts itself at different levels on different objects. For example, a kilogram of mass on the near or the far side of the earth to the moon and a kilogram at the center of the earth all have different forces exerted on them by the moon.

2) The water on the side of the earth near the moon is literally pulled away from the earth, while the earth is literally pulled away from the water on the far side.

3) Because water has to flow around land, it takes a while for the water to flow into bays. This means high tide generally lags behind when the moon is directly overhead.

4) The sun produces tides that are about 50% smaller than the ones produced by the moon. If the sun and moon work together, tides are larger. If the earth, the sun, and the moon form right angles in the sky (half moon), the tides are 50% lower. The extra-high tides, spring tides, can allow people to go farther out on the seafloor at low tide, but may cause flooding at high tide.

Tides are fascinating phenomena but are rarely understood by students. They are caused by the difference in force between the near side and the far side of the earth. Tidal effects would be much larger if the moon were closer to the earth. This would make the difference in force between the near and far side greater, so the tides would be higher or lower. Tidal effects become huge when you get near a black hole because you can get much closer to the center of the object and the mass is much larger.

Tidal effects occur in the earth as well as on the oceans. Because the earth is quite solid, the tide only raises the solid surface a centimeter or so. This is hardly noticeable, except with very sensitive instruments. However, when there are spring tides, there is more motion that causes more stress in the earth. Slightly more earthquakes than average occur during spring tides because of this stress.

Large tides occur in some places, such as the Bay of Fundy, because the period of the tides flowing in and out happens to be the time between high tides. A "standing wave" of large amplitude is set up in much the same way that a standing wave is set up in a musical instrument. Some frequencies make standing waves with large amplitudes that can be heard, while the other frequencies are not. The Bay of Fundy happens to be the proper length to set up a standing wave. If it were longer or shorter, the tides would be much smaller. Similar large tides occur in Cook Inlet near Anchorage, Alaska, and in the Gulf of California. The bays are not quite the right length, so their tides aren't as large as in the Bay of Fundy.

You may want to discuss the fact that the gravitational force acts on both objects. If the earth exerts a gravitational force on the moon, the moon exerts a gravitational force of the **same size** on the earth. It may seem strange that the forces are the same size, but it is true. The earth exerts a gravitational force on you and you exert a force on the earth. Then why do you fall down after you jump into the air; why doesn't the earth "fall up" to you? Actually the earth does, it is just that it doesn't move as far as you do because it has much more mass, about 10^{23} times more.

8

Why Astronauts Become Weightless in a Spacecraft

The term *weightless* is often misunderstood and improperly used. If you were weightless, no gravitational force would be exerted on you. Do astronauts really become weightless as they orbit the earth? If they don't become weightless, how do they float around in the spaceship?

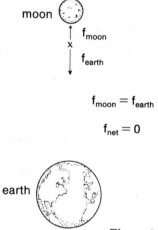

$$f_{moon} = f_{earth}$$
$$f_{net} = 0$$

To be weightless, or with no gravitational force exerted on you, you have to be in special places. At one spot between the moon and the earth, the moon pulls on a mass with the same force as the earth. Because they pull in opposite directions, the net force is zero (if the force from the sun is ignored). At that spot, you would be weightless, as shown in Figure 8a.

Figure 8a

But if the astronauts don't feel any force on them as they orbit the earth, aren't they weightless? The answer is no. They are in *free-fall.* They are falling at the same rate toward the earth as the spacecraft, so they are in *zero g.* They experience no acceleration relative to the spacecraft.

Figure 8b

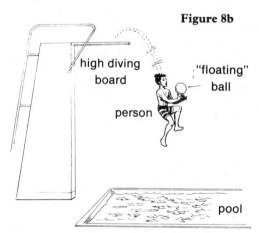

You could have an experience similar to that of the astronauts (for a shorter period of time) if you jumped off a high diving board. (Just think about this, don't go out and do it now!) If you placed a ball on top of your hand and then jumped, the ball would seem to "float" above your hand, as shown in Figure 8b. You wouldn't feel the acceleration and the ball would seem weightless in front of your eyes. In actual fact, both the ball and you would be accelerating. You would change your velocity by 10 meters per second every second (32 feet per second per second). So would the ball. This acceleration is the *g,* or the acceleration due to gravity.

How Everyday Things Work

So how does a spacecraft stay in free-fall for so long? The answer is that *it* is moving around the earth. In one second a person falls about 5 meters (16 ft). The spacecraft in low orbit falls about the same distance, but in that one second it moves horizontally. It moves far enough so the curve of the earth has made the surface of the earth 5 meters farther away. A spacecraft falls 5 meters, but the earth's surface drops five meters. The spacecraft is still the same distance from the earth. An astronaut literally "falls" around the earth, as shown in Figure 8c.

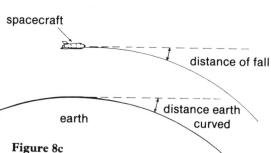

Figure 8c

The spacecraft falls at the same rate the astronaut falls. They fall together just as the ball falls with the diver. (The diver wouldn't feel any weight either, but the weightless experience would last for a second or so, instead of for many orbits of the earth.)

If an astronaut takes a space walk, the astronaut orbits with the spacecraft. The space walker is really a small satellite orbiting beside the larger spacecraft. Gravity makes them both fall toward the earth at the same rate.

Astronauts "feel" weightless even though there is a gravitational force on them. They move with the spacecraft, so there is no force exerted on them by the spacecraft. If they are doing something and need to leave a tool somewhere for a minute, they can leave it "hanging" in the air. When they come back to it, it will still be there. When you are in free-fall, you do not feel your weight. You don't have to exert any force on the ball "floating" in front of you in order to keep it there. It stays there on its own.

One problem with this floating condition is that muscles and bones start to weaken as a result of lack of use. Muscles and bones are not put under any stress at all. The weakening of bones and muscles becomes a problem on long trips in space. Russian astronauts (who have spent longer periods of time in space than anyone else) have had difficulty getting used to gravity again because of weak bones and muscles. Even though they exercise, their bodies change and are weaker when they return. Research is still going on to find ways to keep the body active and healthy in space.

Review Questions

1) Where could you be truly weightless and why would this be so?
2) How does free-fall explain the way astronauts feel in a spacecraft?
3) Why don't astronauts feel any force on them when they orbit the earth?
4) How could you experience weightlessness here on earth?

TEACHER

Answers

1) Between the earth and the moon (about 90% of the way to the moon from earth), the gravitational force of the moon would equal the force from the earth. You would be weightless.

2) The spacecraft is falling as fast as the astronaut as they orbit the earth. In the same way that a ball will float above your hand as you jump off a high diving board, no force is exerted on the ball to keep it there.

3) Astronauts fall as fast as the spacecraft toward the earth, so no forces are needed to keep them moving with the spacecraft.

4) You could jump off a high diving board.

The term "weightless" is constantly used improperly by non-physicists. The correct way to talk about what happens in orbiting spacecraft is to say that astronauts are in *free-fall* or *zero g*, where g is the acceleration due to gravity. Relative to the spacecraft, they are not accelerating. Therefore, no force from the spacecraft is exerted on them. They don't feel the force of gravity because they are accelerating toward the earth with the spacecraft. If you are not accelerating relative to the earth, a force must be exerted on you by the ground, bed, or other object to oppose gravity.

Students should learn why things seem to float around in an orbiting spaceship. It is because everything is falling at the same rate that everything appears to float. It is possible to model the jump off a high diving board on a smaller scale in the classroom. Stand on a chair or table and hold a small object on top of your hand. Then jump. The object will float over your hand as you fall. Students will find that they see both you and the pencil falling. The pencil "floats" for the exact same reason that the things in an orbiting spacecraft float. They are all accelerating at the same rate. Because the relative acceleration is zero, they fall together.

Astronauts get practice working in zero g by taking flights in a specially-padded airplane. The plane starts by flying upward and then follows a parabolic path, which eventually takes it down. You can get about 20 seconds of free-fall on each one of these parabolic falls. The plane pulls out of the dive and repeats the process, up to ten times in a row. (This kind of flying tends to make people airsick.) Many students think that gravity can be turned off in some way, but no one has found a way to conteract gravity. If such a method were found, it would have vast economic importance. Planes and rockets could be launched with ease. Obviously, no such method has been found, though students will believe that it exists. They have seen lots of movies. . . .

The results of zero g on people for extended periods of time can be very damaging. Diet and exercise do not seem to completely prevent the effects of the lack of stress on bones and muscles. This problem will have to be overcome if we are to visit Mars, for instance. The trip to Mars will take longer than the amount of time anyone has orbited the earth.

9

How Cross-Country Ski Wax Works

You may not realize it, but cross-country skis pose a curious problem. The ski must have traction to be able to get going in the first place, but it must be able to slide freely in order to move. One approach to solving this problem was the "fish-scale" or "waxless" ski. The bottom of the ski has numerous raised scallops, like the scales of a fish. If you run your hand over these scales, you will find that it is easy to move your hand one way, but hard to move in the other direction. On snow, this works to give you enough traction to push off, as the ski resists moving over the snow, but as you move off, the snow glides past the scales in the right direction to reduce friction.

Unfortunately, these waxless skis are often not as fast as a well-waxed ski, and they work best in a packed track. If you are not on a packed track, the old-fashioned wax is often the best way to move easily over the snow. Wax on cross-country skis allows you to stick when you want to push off, but it is slippery when you want the ski to slide. Specialized waxes, generally of different colors, are used under various weather and snow conditions to make this happen. But how does the wax work?

Figure 9a

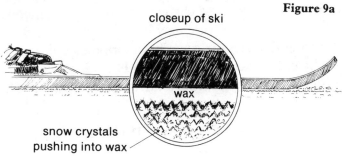

closeup of ski

wax

snow crystals
pushing into wax

Basically, the wax is soft enough so that when it is pressed into the snow, snow crystals push into the wax. The wax becomes "interlocked" with the snow so it doesn't slide easily, as shown in Figure 9a. Then, when you want the ski to slide, you start the ski sliding over the snow and the wax then smooths out. It becomes a smooth-sliding surface. The wax is literally made rough and then smooth every time you take a stride.

Different kinds of waxes are used because snow comes in many different forms. When snow falls at temperatures well below freezing, it has many small sharp crystals. Over time, the crystals become more rounded. The change occurs because individual molecules in the crystals melt and move to different places. The melting occurs because a molecule, through collisions with other molecules, gets enough energy to break its solid bonds. It doesn't happen very often, but it happens enough to change the shape of the crystals.

　　　　23

Because water likes to form spheres (or drops) when the individual molecules melt, they move to make the crystal round. After they move, they refreeze. As time goes by, snow crystals become rounder and rounder. The rounding process occurs more rapidly on warm days because more molecules melt when the temperature is warmer.

Figure 9b

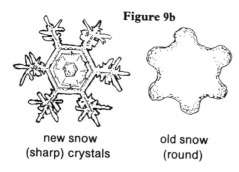

new snow
(sharp) crystals

old snow
(round)

Different kinds of snow are shaped differently, as shown in Figure 9b. Sharp crystals of cold, fresh snow push into wax easily, so a "hard" wax is used. The hard wax makes a very thin layer on the ski. Because the crystals make very small impressions in the wax, the impressions can be smoothed out easily. The wax is very fast when it glides. Old snow tends to have more rounded crystals, so the wax must be softer for the crystals to push into it. This wax is more goopy and tends to stick to everything.

Special waxes must be used if the snow has frozen. For this snow a "klister," which sticks very firmly to the ski, is used. This is needed because the icy snow is very abrasive and quickly takes wax off the ski.

Waxing skis is a bit more difficult than using waxless skis because when the snow conditions change, you have to change your wax. On a cold morning, the snow temperature may be way below freezing. As the temperature warms during the day, the snow has more molecules in the liquid state at the surface. The crystals change shape and become rounder, so you need to use a softer wax. This is done by putting a different wax over the first layer.

Review Questions

1) What happens to snow crystals as time passes and why?

2) How do cross-country ski waxes allow you to stick when you need to and slide when you need to?

3) As the temperature warms up, what might you have to do to keep your skis working properly?

4) What do you need on your skis if the snow is icy? Why?

How Everyday Things Work

TEACHER

Answers

1) Snow crystals become rounder over time because individual molecules break their solid bonds and enter the liquid phase. Surface tension then makes them tend to form spheres, which makes the crystals rounder.

2) The waxes allow the crystals to bite into them when you press down to get traction, but they smooth out when you start sliding.

3) You need to put on a softer wax because the crystals become larger and rounder. The softer wax then allows the rounder crystals to grip.

4) You must use klister, which sticks firmly to the ski and doesn't wear off.

Cross-country ski wax is an interesting material. Each brand has a slightly different formula and, as you might expect, they all behave a little differently with each kind of snow. Some waxes work well in new snow, while others with slightly different characteristics work best in old snow.

The change in character of snow crystals occurs continuously. It occurs even at very cold temperatures because occasionally, at random, some water molecule gains enough energy to break the solid bonds. The molecule of water can then briefly flow before it refreezes. Drops of water tend to form spheres because surface tension tries to reduce the surface area of the drop to the smallest amount. When the molecule becomes liquid, it works toward making the surface of the crystal smaller. This makes the crystal rounder.

Many people are not aware of the changes that occur in snow crystals. Even at cold temperatures, snow can disappear by sublimation (the transfer directly from the solid to the gas state). Frozen carbon dioxide (dry ice) normally does this. However, when temperatures are below freezing, especially when the snow is in the sun, some molecules gain enough energy to break the bonds and turn into gas molecules. The snow can disappear.

If you have a variety of ski waxes available, students will be interested in seeing the differences between the types of wax. You can read about the temperature ranges for the waxes on the tubes and then compare their consistencies.

10

How Trees Stand Up in Wind

When the wind blows through the trees, you might wonder how they can keep standing. Obviously, roots hold the trees upright, but what physics laws keep them standing?

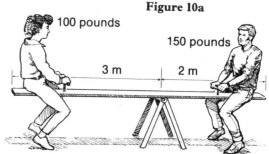

Figure 10a

100 pounds

150 pounds

3 m   2 m

100 pounds × 3 m = 150 pounds × 2 m

It may seem strange, but the physics of why trees stand is the same as the physics of how a seesaw works. The seesaw balances when the *torques* are balanced and starts to rotate when they are not. A torque is similar to a force, except that it causes things to turn or rotate instead of accelerating them in a straight line. Torque is the product of force times the distance from the support (or axis of rotation), as shown in Figure 10a (force × distance = torque). Seesaws rotate about an axis when you apply a torque.

When two people of equal weight sit on a seesaw, the axis of rotation is where the center of the board sits on the support. The two people sit an equal distance from the support. The product of the weight times the distance between one person and the support equals the product of the other person's weight times the distance he or she is from the support. The torque from one person **balances** the torque from the other, so the seesaw balances. If one person weighs more than the other, that person must sit closer to the center than the lighter one. Again, the torques must balance.

To make the seesaw move, one person pushes against the ground. This force at a distance from the support causes unbalanced torque. The torque causes rotation; one end goes up and the other goes down. When the other person exerts a force with his or her feet, it causes another torque. This stops the rotation and makes the rotation go in the opposite direction.

How Everyday Things Work

Figure 10b

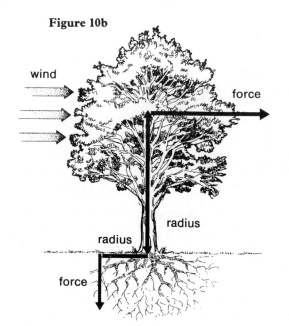

Trees are like seesaws because the trees' roots oppose the torque produced by the wind, as shown in Figure 10b. The roots are anchored to the ground by dirt and other trees' roots that intertwine as weights. This weight provides a torque that keeps the tree upright against the torque from the wind. If the wind is too strong, the roots may pull out of the ground or break off. If this happens, the tree falls.

You can build a model seesaw using a meterstick and some small weights. Experiment to find what combinations of weights and positions allow your seesaw to balance. What is needed to get the seesaw to turn? You might run your experiments in the playground and see if your model seesaw works like a full-scale seesaw.

TEACHER

Materials Needed
metersticks blocks   supports weights

When students make a model of a seesaw, they should make sure that the meterstick is supported in the middle, as shown in Figure 10c. You may need something larger than a pencil for the support if the meterstick bends. The stick should be sup-

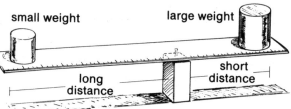

Figure 10c

ported by a small point and be free to rotate. The weights can be any convenient objects, but they should be of the same size or in set intervals of weight. If the weights are not labeled and vary in weight, the conclusions the students draw may be incorrect.

As you run the lab, guide the students toward finding where two weights must be placed to balance one weight, etc. They should look for numerical relationships. This helps them to visualize torques and also helps them to look for the mathematical relationship that governs seesaws.

A seesaw is a simple machine. Basically, it is a lever that is ridden instead of used to lift something. The same principles that govern levers govern a seesaw.

A torque is the product of force times distance from the axis. (This is only true when the force is exerted perpendicularly to the lever arm.) This is basically the case with a seesaw, so the equation works well for this exercise.

The importance of having the force acting perpendicularly to the lever arm can be shown quite easily. If you hold a meterstick horizontally with your fingers, one hand holding each end, observe what happens when you drop one end. Gravity exerts a force that acts at a distance from the support. The force is

Figure 10d

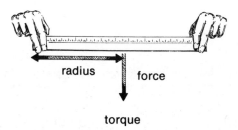

radius · force

torque

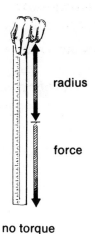

radius

force

no torque

at right angles to the axis, so there is a torque. The meterstick starts to rotate. Now, hold the meterstick from one end with the other end pointing vertically down. A force is still exerted on the meterstick, but it is parallel to the axis. The result this time is that the meterstick does not want to turn. There is no torque when the force is parallel to the radius on which it acts, as shown in Figure 10d.

11

How Soap Cleans

Soap is wonderful stuff. It attaches water and grease, which don't normally mix, and allows the water to take the grease down the drain. But how does it do this?

A soap molecule is interesting in that it has a *polar* end and a *nonpolar* end. The polar end grabs onto water and the nonpolar end grabs onto grease. But what do polar and nonpolar mean? You might say a polar substance is electrically active. The surface has areas that are either positively or negatively charged. As you might expect, a nonpolar substance has neither a positive nor a negative charge on its surface.

Water is an example of a polar substance. The two hydrogen atoms and one oxygen atom (H_2O) are not in a line, as shown in Figure 11a. Because the oxygen atom pulls harder on the electrons than the hydrogen atoms do, it sort of *steals* them. The oxygen atom becomes negative (the charge on electrons is negative) while the hydrogen atoms become positive. The molecule becomes polar because it is positive at one end and negative at the other.

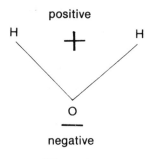

Figure 11a

Grease is nonpolar because the atoms are symmetrically placed and no electrons are pulled to any side. Because polar molecules attach easily to other polar molecules but cannot bond to nonpolar ones, grease and water don't mix. Nonpolar molecules want to attach to other nonpolar molecules, which is why grease holds together.

Figure 11b

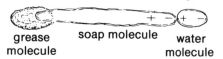

grease molecule   soap molecule   water molecule

Now what about soap? Because a soap molecule is polar on one end and is nonpolar on the other, one end can bond to the grease and the other end can bond to the water, as shown in Figure 11b. When the water goes down the drain, the grease goes too. For every grease molecule you want to remove from a greasy plate, you need one soap molecule to attach it to the water. Soap acts as a bridge between the two. If you are washing dishes in a sink and they aren't getting clean, adding more soap adds more molecules that can grab onto the remaining grease and wash it away.

Review Questions

1) What is a polar and what is a nonpolar substance?

2) How do polar and nonpolar substances bond to each other?

3) How does soap remove grease?

TEACHER

Answers

1) A polar substance has positively or negatively charged surfaces. A nonpolar substance has neither a positive nor negative charge on its surface.

2) Polar substances bond to polar ones and nonpolar substances bond to nonpolar ones. Polar and nonpolar substances don't bond.

3) Soap has a polar end and a nonpolar end. This allows it to bond to both grease and water at the same time. It acts like a bridge between these two substances that normally don't mix.

The interesting properties of soap that allow it to clean are a common application of chemistry. Detergents work in much the same way, using chemicals to get grease or oil to mix with water.

Soap is actually made from a fat, which is then chemically altered to give it a polar part. The fat is nonpolar, so that end attaches to grease while the added polar part attaches to the water.

The bonding of polar substances occurs because the positive part of one molecule wants to be close to the negative part of another molecule. This electrical attraction allows the bond to form. Nonpolar bonding occurs with van der Waals forces and tends to be a weaker bond than polar bonding.

Soaps also help in the cleaning process in other ways. When cleaning fabric, soap reduces water's surface tension, which makes it easier for the water to get between the cloth fibers and clean them. Surface tension is reduced because the water molecules cannot hold onto each other as tightly when the soap is present. Reducing surface tension also allows soap bubbles to form. Normally, water bubbles are small because the surface tension of water is so strong. Reducing the surface tension allows large bubbles to form. If the bubbles disappear when you are washing dishes, then all the soap has grease attached to it, so it no longer reduces the surface tension. You have to add more soap.

Electric Shocks and Doorknobs

When you walk across a rug and then touch a metal object, you sometimes get a small shock. Most of the time you don't. What causes the shock? Why don't you get shocked every time you touch a piece of metal? When you walk across a wool rug in rubber-soled shoes, you separate electrical charges. When you touch the metal object, the charges move again. We see a spark when the charges move.

Electrical charges behave in predictable ways. Like charges repel. Because electrons all have a negative charge, electrons repel each other. Opposite charges attract, so a positive charge and a negative charge attract each other.

Shocks often cause a funny feeling in your finger. This feeling occurs because an electrical charge is moving through your finger as a small current. Nerves carry messages because of electrical charges changing positions in them. The current in your finger confuses the messages carried by the nerves. Often, the nerves that fire are ones associated with pain. Ouch!

Why do the charges separate when your shoe rubs on the carpet? Well, rubber tends to take electrons away from the wool in the rug. When the rubber picks up extra electrons (which are negative), we say the rubber is *negatively charged*. Some of the negative charge picked up by the rubber soles is transferred to you. You then become negatively charged. It is this negative charge that forms the small spark when you touch a metal object.

negatively charged fingers

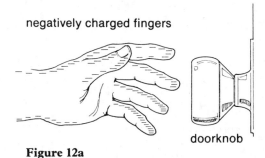

doorknob

Figure 12a

When you touch a metal object, electrons jump to the metal because like charges repel. Negative charges in your finger move away from the other negative charges in the rest of your body and jump to the metal, as shown in Figure 12a.

Sometimes you don't get shocked when you touch metal. This means that either no charge is picked up by the rubber in your shoes or the charge leaked off you. The most common cause of this leaking charge is moisture. When the air is humid (full of water vapor) you hardly ever get a shock on a doorknob. Moisture also makes it harder for the rubber in your shoes to pick up charge. On humid days there is always a bit of moisture on everything. Any charge that builds up on your shoes is quickly lost.

Because moisture allows current to flow more easily, you should never take electrical appliances into the bathtub or use them near water. Water may allow the electricity that runs the appliance to get out of the appliance and into you. This electric current is much larger than the current you feel when you get a shock touching a doorknob. It can cause the nerves in your body to fire randomly or paralyze nerves that regulate your heartbeat. If the current makes these nerves fire at improper times, your heart may stop or beat so rapidly that you die from heart failure. Your heart literally tires itself out and then stops beating.

You can run some simple experiments to see how charges separate. Take two pieces of plastic wrap and wrap a small amount of each piece around a pencil leaving a large "flag" hanging off, as shown in Figure 12b. Note what happens when you bring your two "flags" near each other. Rub the flags on your hair and repeat the experiment. What is the result?

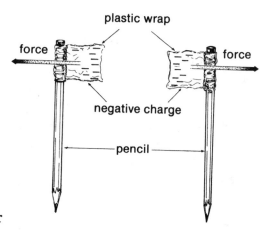

Figure 12b

Try rubbing other objects against each other and see which ones attract or repel the plastic flag. If the charge on the plastic is negative, what is the charge on the other objects that you bring near your flag? After you have tried all of the available materials, put a small amount of water on one object you found could be charged. Now see if you can charge it.

Review Questions

1) What happens when two negatively charged objects are near each other? two positively charged objects?

2) Why might your fingers move when you get shocked?

3) How does rubber become negatively charged after rubbing wool?

4) What happens to the flow of electricity when your hands are wet as compared to dry?

5) What causes the shock you get sometimes when you touch a doorknob?

How Everyday Things Work

```
┌─────────────────────┐
│                     │
│      TEACHER        │
│                     │
└─────────────────────┘
```

Materials Needed		
plastic wrap	pencils	materials for "rubbing"

Answers

1) Like charges repel.

2) Nerves operate on electrical impulses; when current flows through them, they cause muscles to twitch.

3) Electrons are removed from the wool and are attached to the rubber.

4) Moisture, especially moisture with ions in it, makes current flow easily. (Sweat has lots of charged particles called ions in it.) The small static charges that get on you quickly flow off when the humidity is high.

5) Shocks are caused by the rubber in the shoes picking up a negative charge, which then flows off you to the doorknob. This flow of current causes the nerves in your finger, which operate on electrical impulses, to fire.

This segment on static electricity helps to explain why sparks occur when you touch things. Running any static electricity experiments may be frustrating, however, unless you have a dry day. Humidity makes it more difficult to separate charges. The plastic wrap generally picks up charge, so the two flags should repel (they are charged the same), but other things may not become charged.

In preparing for this lab, you should try to get a wide variety of materials that can be rubbed on each other: plastic sheets, wool, rubber, glass, silk, pencils, wood, metal, etc. Some of these objects will pick up charge and others won't. The variety is important. Objects that pick up charge and keep it are called *insulators*. Conductors, like metal, allow any charge to quickly move off the person holding it. People are not great conductors, but they will conduct electricity.

Students must understand that like charges repel and unlike, or opposite, charges attract. If they know these rules, they can indicate which charges are brought near the flags. When charges are separated, the objects are said to be *charged*. When the objects go back to their uncharged state, they are said to be *neutralized*.

You should have the students think about how they are getting charges from certain objects. In particular, if they rub a piece of rubber (like a shoe) on wool, the rubber should become negatively charged and repel the flag. However, if the wool is brought near the flag, it will attract the flag because it has become positively charged, as it gave up electrons to the rubber.

You should try to focus the students' attention on what happens if there is humidity or dampness. This alerts students to the danger of using electrical appliances near water. The electric building code requires special circuits that include devices called *Ground Fault Interrupters* to be used in places where water may come in contact with electrical appliances. These circuits (discussed in another section) shut off current if, for example, a person is getting shocked.

Your students might be interested in how a lie detector works. Basically, electrodes (wires) are connected to the skin. A small voltage is applied and a current flows. If the skin is dry, there is more resistance to current flow so little current flows. If the person sweats, the skin gets wet and becomes a better conductor, thus more current flows. It is assumed that people sweat a little when they tell lies. Therefore, if the current increases, the person lied. The problem with this test is that some people sweat because they are nervous about the test.

13

Lightning

We all know that thunder is produced by lightning, but what causes lightning?

Lightning is a big spark that moves either between one cloud and another or between a cloud and the ground. The spark carries a great deal of electrical charge, and each charge has energy. If all the energy of the lightning bolt were used to lift an average person in the air, the person would be lifted more than five miles high!

Although it may sound a bit strange, scientists still do not know exactly what causes lightning. They have a pretty good theory, but it is not perfect. The theory states that charges separate in raindrops (or ice crystals) because of the earth's electric field. This allows each raindrop (or ice crystal) to pick up negative charge as it falls in the cloud. The negative charge is brought to the bottom of a cloud where it is left. When enough charge builds up at the bottom of the cloud, a spark forms between the cloud and ground and produces lightning.

You may not have understood that last paragraph. Let's learn about lightning a bit more slowly. First, we learned that like charges repel and opposite charges attract. Two negative charges (*like charges*) are repelled—they want to move apart. If you place a positive charge near a negative charge (*opposite charges*), they are attracted.

Knowing how charged particles move when they are near other charges allows us to see what happens to the charges in a raindrop. The whole earth is negatively charged. This causes negative charges in the raindrop to be repelled from the earth and move to the top of the drop. Positive charges (opposite from the charge on the earth) move toward the earth. This makes the raindrop look like the one in Figure 13a, with the negative charges on the top and positive charges on the bottom.

Figure 13a

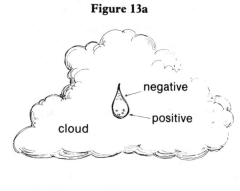

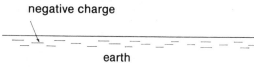

How Everyday Things Work

Figure 13b

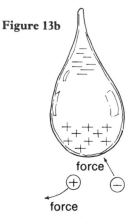

The air through which a raindrop falls is never pure. It has some positively charged and some negatively charged particles in it. As the drop falls, the positive bottom of the drop runs into both positively and negatively charged particles. What does it do when it meets them? The positive charge at the bottom of the drop repels positive particles but attracts negative particles. The negative particles move toward the drop and stick to it, as shown in Figure 13b. The positive particles would like to stick to the top of the drop, but they have a problem. They have to move out of the way of the drop because of like-charge repulsion. They must then move toward the top of the drop and grab on. This is difficult for the same reason that more insects land on the front windshield of a car than on the rear window. The positive particles cannot get to the drop whereas the negative particles can. This makes the drop pick up negative charge.

Each drop picks up only a little charge, but there are many raindrops. The result is that lots of charge collects at the bottom of the cloud. The bottom of the cloud becomes negative.

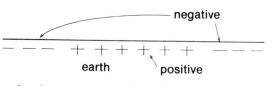

Figure 13c

But a question still hasn't been answered. How does this negative charge go to the normally negative earth? The answer is that like charges repel. When the negative charge gathers in the cloud, the negative charge in the earth briefly moves away from under the cloud. As shown in Figure 13c, the ground under the cloud becomes positive. The negative charges in the cloud are then attracted to the ground. They move as a lightning bolt.

If you stand under a cloud that is ready to send a lightning bolt to the ground, your hair may stand on end. The earth is positive and because you are touching the earth, you also become positive. Even your hair becomes positive.

How Everyday Things Work

The negative charge in the cloud attracts your hair. **If your hair ever stands on end, you are in real danger!** Immediately get into a building or lie down on the ground and curl into a ball. This may save you from injury.

Review Questions

1) How are sparks and lightning similar?

2) What do like charges do and what do opposite charges do?

3) Where are the positive and negative charges in a raindrop? What does the drop pick up as it falls?

4) How does lightning go to the normally negative earth?

5) What does it mean when your hair stands on end and why does it occur?

TEACHER

Answers

1) Both a spark and lightning are electrical charges moving through the air.

2) Like charges repel and opposite charges attract.

3) Positive charges move to the bottom of the drop and negative ones move to the top. This causes the drop to pick up negative charges by opposite-charge attraction.

4) The negative charges in the cloud force negative charges in the ground away, making it positive. The negative charges in the cloud then move toward the positively charged ground.

5) It means that the ground and your hair are positive and your hair is attracted to the negatively charged cloud. Lightning is imminent. Seek shelter immediately.

The theory on lightning is not complete. One of the problems with developing a theory is that it is difficult to gather good data on what lightning does and what is happening in a cloud. This is because it is dangerous to go into clouds that are producing lightning. Lightning is so energetic that it destroys equipment when it strikes.

After an *Atlas Centaur* rocket was destroyed as a result of a lightning strike at Cape Canaveral, researchers began studying lightning in that area by firing small rockets trailing wires into clouds ready to release bolts. (This is an experiment similar to Ben Franklin's, but they used wire instead of silk. The researchers are also a little more careful than Franklin, who could easily have killed himself running the experiment.) These experiments and many others are beginning to give us a better feel for what conditions in a cloud make it ready to give off a bolt of lightning, but scientists still haven't perfected the theory.

The separation of charges in the drops occurs because earth's negative charge is actually enhanced when the upper atmosphere is positively charged. After a while, the top of the cloud becomes positive and the bottom negative, as shown in Figure 13d on page 41. Charge inside the cloud separates the charges in the drops even more than the earth's charge does.

The drops pick up charges and then deposit them at the bottom of the cloud. This removal of charge from the drops may occur because the charge resides on the outside of the drop (like-charge repulsion). When the drop falls below the cloud, it starts to evaporate and the charge is taken with the evaporating water. Updrafts then take the charge to the bottom of the cloud.

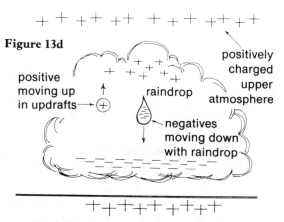

Figure 13d

positively charged upper atmosphere

positive moving up in updrafts →

raindrop

negatives moving down with raindrop

The motion of charge on the ground occurs because the earth is a relatively good conductor of electric current. The negatively charged cloud can induce negative charges to leave the area under the cloud. When negative charges leave, positive charge remains, leaving the ground positive. Sometimes a "return stroke" can be observed as positively charged ions move upward to meet the descending group of electrons.

Once the bolt strikes the ground, the charges move away from the point of impact. The currents and voltages can be large. The voltages can be strong enough to knock a person down even a long way from where the lightning strikes. People might say that they were struck by lightning and survived. While they might have experienced the effects of the bolt, they actually had little chance of surviving if they had been directly hit by a bolt.

14
Simple Switches

Lights and other electrical appliances need to be turned on and off. A simple switch can do this, but how does such a switch work?

It may help you to think about switches if you think about what they do. Electric current flows in metal wires. Metals and some other substances are called *conductors.* Current normally doesn't flow through the air or through substances considered *insulators,* such as glass, plastic, or rubber.

A switch is a mechanism that sometimes permits the electric current to flow through a wire and sometimes prevents it from flowing. When the switch is off, there is a small "gap" in the wire carrying the current. The current can't bridge this gap, therefore the power is "off." The gap can be closed by a piece of metal, which makes the switch turn "on."

It is dangerous to touch most wires because of the possibility of electric shock. However, you can safely handle wires attached to a flashlight battery. Use wires, tape, a light bulb, and a flashlight battery to demonstrate how a switch works. Connect a wire from one end of the battery to the light, using tape to hold the wires to the battery. Then connect a wire from the other end of the battery to the other connection for the light bulb. The light should go on.

Figure 14

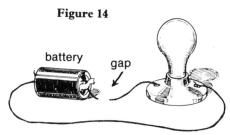

battery   gap

Make a small gap between one end of the battery and the wire, as shown in Figure 14. The "switch" is now open. Take a small piece of aluminum foil and use it to fill the gap. The light should go on when the foil touches both sides of the gap. Test other materials to see which allow the light to go on. These are conductors. Materials that do not allow the light to go on are insulators.

WARNING: Do not connect a wire directly from one end of the battery to the other. It will cause the battery to get hot and it might explode. It will also ruin the battery.

How Everyday Things Work

TEACHER

Materials Needed

wire   a light bulb

tape   batteries

materials to test as insulators and conductors

Simple switches come in many different forms. Some slide, some turn, and some, like most hallway light switches, are "rocker" types. They all work the same way: they either connect or disconnect wires so that current can or cannot flow.

It is easy to see how some switches work, and you may have an example of one of these types in the general science lab. It may help to demonstrate one or two of these switches. An old-style telegraph key is a good example. You can make one out of a strip of metal which can be pushed down to make a connection and then springs back when you release pressure. Instead of having a piece of metal fill the gap, you get rid of the gap.

This simple activity might be better used as a demonstration rather than a hands-on activity for the older students. However, it is a good starting point for younger students, particularly if they are going to work with a two-way switch in the following exercise. (A two-way switch allows a light to be turned on and off from two places.)

Provide the students with a large assortment of materials to test to see which materials allow current to flow across the gap. Examples are paper, plastic, metal objects, wood, etc. The greater the variety, the better.

WARNING: Electricity can be dangerous. **Playing with wires other than those attached to flashlight batteries can be deadly.** Make sure that students do not connect a wire from one end of the battery to the other. This short-circuits the battery and can cause the battery to heat up and explode. This danger demands proper supervision.

15

A Two-Way Light Switch

Lights in rooms or halls often need to be turned on or off from two places. You want to turn on a light when you start down the hall and turn it off when you reach the other end. To be able to do this, you need a *two-way switch.*

How does this special kind of switch work? Can you build one yourself? This activity shows you how to build a model of one and to use it to turn a light off and on.

The switch requires a special electric cable. Most electric cables have two wires carrying current. Current flows one way in one and the other way in the other. When two switches must turn a light on and off, three wires are needed to carry current. One wire always carries current while the other two alternate in carrying current.

Figure 15

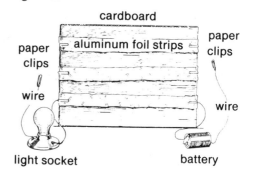

Although you should never touch bare wires coming from electrical outlets in the wall, you can safely work with wires attached to a flashlight battery. You can make a two-way switch using three long aluminum foil strips, a piece of cardboard, and paper clips. Use the paper clips to hold the strips on a piece of cardboard, as shown in Figure 15.

Attach one wire from the light bulb to one end of the lowest aluminum strip. Another wire from the battery is attached to just a paper clip. The battery is connected to the other end of the lowest aluminum strip with a wire and with another wire going to a paper clip. (Connect wires to the foil strips using paper clips.)

Now you can model the switch. The paper clips attached to wires connect to either the upper piece of foil or the middle piece of foil. This is similar to what occurs when a two-way switch is pushed up or down. Start with both paper clips at opposite ends of the top piece of foil. Is the light on? Now, move one switch (a paper clip) to the lower wire. Is the light on? Experiment to see what combinations of positions of the paper clips turn the light on. Record your observations about which connections cause the bulb to light. How do you think the switching is done in an actual light switch?

Materials Needed

aluminum foil	light bulb
cardboard	1.5 volt battery
paper clips	battery and lamp holders (optional)

This section shows students how two switches can operate one light. The wiring is shown to the students and they can experiment to see what combinations of switch positions cause a light to go on. Basically, the light is on if both switches are up or both switches are down. If one is up and the other is down, then the light is off.

The equipment to demonstrate this is rather simple and although it can be done with wires instead of foil strips, the strips allow the students to see more clearly how the switch works. Because the foil is clipped to cardboard, it stays in place, whereas wires tend to become twisted.

The aluminum foil can be cut either beforehand (for speed) or by the students during the activity. The battery should be a 1.5 volt cell and the light should be appropriate for the battery. Battery and lamp holders make things much easier.

Students should write down their observations about what is happening in their "circuits." Once a few students get their circuits going, they can help other students. Do be careful, however, that the students who are shown how to do it really understand what is being done. If they don't understand how the circuit works, they may continue to think that this kind of switch is magic.

If you are short on time, you may want to set up the three foil strips and make the connections before the students start work.

WARNING: Working with electricity can be dangerous. **Playing with wires other than those attached to flashlight batteries can be deadly.** Proper supervision is mandatory. You should also make sure that students do not short-circuit the battery by connecting a wire from one end of the battery to the other. This can cause the battery to heat up and explode.

16

Ground Fault Interrupter Circuit (GFIC)

In many bathrooms and kitchens, there are different-looking electrical outlets. They have the regular two sockets but they also have some buttons. These special outlets guard against electric shocks. If someone touches a wire and starts to have electric current flow through him or her, the GFIC immediately cuts off the current. This can prevent the person from being electrocuted most of the time. How does this device operate? What "tells" it that someone is getting a shock?

A *Ground Fault Interrupter Circuit* (GFIC) cuts off current when more electricity flows into the circuit than flows out of it. Normally, all the current that flows along one wire comes back on the other. If the same amount of current flows in as flows out, then no current gets lost. Lost current can be current going through a person (the person is getting a shock). Building a GFIC is not easy because very small amounts of current can kill a person. Therefore, the device must be able to find small differences in current going in and out of the circuit. When it has detected a difference, it shuts off the current very quickly in order to protect the person.

A GFIC works because the two wires carrying current in a circuit are near a coil of wire. The coil has many turns of very fine wire. If the wires carry the same current in opposite directions, their magnetic fields cancel. If one carries more than the other, a magnetic field is produced. The coil senses any change in the current in the wires by sensing a change in magnetic field.

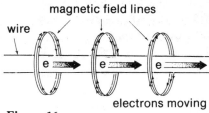

magnetic field lines

wire

electrons moving

Figure 16a

Any wire carrying current produces a magnetic field, as shown in Figure 16a. However, the fields in most straight wires are hardly noticeable and a coil of wire is needed to observe the fields. Electromagnets make strong fields in this way. You may have made an electromagnet by wrapping a coil of wire around a nail and connecting it to a battery. It picked up iron and steel objects with magnetic force when current flowed but when you disconnected the wires, the objects dropped.

If two wires are side by side carrying current in opposite directions, each wire produces a magnetic field. However, because the current flows in opposite directions, the fields point in opposite directions and cancel. As long as the same current flows in each wire, the magnetic fields cancel. A magnetic field is formed only when one wire has more current than the other.

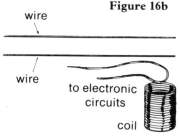

Figure 16b

The coil of wire in the GFIC is placed near the wires carrying current to the circuit, as shown in Figure 16b. If there is a change in the amount of magnetic field that goes through a coil of wire, a current will flow. This change in current is very small when someone is getting shocked because the amount of current needed to shock someone is very small. Transistors are used to amplify this small current. This amplified current is used to break the circuit by opening an electronic switch.

The GFIC must be checked periodically to make sure that the device is operating properly. Because the GFIC is so sensitive, a nearby lightning strike (or other things) can burn out the protective device. Therefore, you should check the GFIC monthly by pushing a test button. This button allows some current to leak out of the circuit similarly to the way someone would get a shock. If the current is stopped, all is well. You push a reset button and your circuit is returned to normal. If the circuit is not broken, then the GFIC should be replaced by an electrician.

WARNING: A GFIC cannot protect against all electric shocks, so you must be careful to prevent them. These devices are used in bathrooms and kitchens, where people are using electrical appliances near water, and outside where people are using electrical tools. While a GFIC can prevent most electric shocks from being serious, it is no excuse for not using proper safety precautions.

Review Questions

1) When are magnetic fields produced by wires carrying current?

2) When do two current-carrying wires produce no magnetic field?

3) How does a GFIC sense that someone is getting shocked?

4) Why do GFIC's need to be checked periodically?

How Everyday Things Work

TEACHER

Answers

1) Magnetic fields are always produced when charges move, whether in a wire or as individual particles.

2) Two wires don't produce a field if they carry the same current in opposite directions. Their fields cancel.

3) The GFIC senses the loss of current by a change in the amount of magnetic field in a coil of wire. Because we use AC current, this field changes direction 60 times per second. This allows the coil to detect a small change in field and open the circuit using transistor circuits.

4) The sensitive circuits may be damaged by large currents or voltages.

This section discusses the GFIC outlet. Most GFIC's work basically the same way. A coil of wire senses when the magnetic field from the wires carrying current in the circuit changes from zero. With equal and opposite currents, the circuit wires should produce magnetic fields that cancel each other. When electric current is lost, then a field will occur.

One thing helps the GFIC in identifying the change in magnetic field. This is that the current is AC, or alternating current. Because the currents go one way and then the other, the magnetic field does too. This means that the slight magnetic field produced by the small current differences changes back and forth 60 times per second. The rapid change in field allows a larger current to form in the GFIC's coil, making it easier to sense.

A changing magnetic field in a coil of wire produces a current. This is how generators work: coils of wire are turned near magnets (or magnets are turned near coils of wire—the effect is the same). Most high school physics texts can give a more complete discussion of why a current is formed. It involves Lenz's Law and Faraday's Law.

Electric shock is dangerous because it affects the nerves. If it affects the nerves controlling the heart, it can stop the heart or cause it to beat wildly, both of which can cause death. Even though electric current is dangerous, birds can sit on power lines because the difference in voltage between the feet of the bird is small, and little current flows through the bird. In some areas in Alaska, people had to redesign power lines so that bald eagles (with large wingspans) didn't touch two wires with different voltage at the same time. This would make a large current flow through the eagle and kill it.

Skin is not very conductive, but water is. GFIC's are used in bathroom circuits because people often use electrical appliances when their hands are wet. With dry skin, it takes a little while before the current literally burns through the skin and makes a better connection, but the GFIC would cut off the current before this happened, just as it does with wet hands.

How Lights Burn Out and Why Halogen Lights Are More Efficient

Light bulbs burn out if they are hit, but they eventually burn out even if they are never disturbed. What causes them to burn out and why do light bulbs like *quartz halogen* bulbs last longer and burn brighter?

A light bulb gives off light because electric current goes through a thin wire called a *filament*. The current heats the wire until it glows and gives off light. For most lights, the temperature of the bulb is about 3500°C. The bulbs give off white light because they are hot. A burner on a stove only gets hot enough to give off a red light. If the temperature of the burner were raised slowly, it would glow orange, yellow, and then finally white-hot.

Things burn rapidly at 3500°C if oxygen is present. Therefore, light bulbs are filled with a gas other than oxygen. The filament must also stay solid and not melt, so it is often made of tungsten. Tungsten has a high melting point so that it stays in the solid form even at 3500°C.

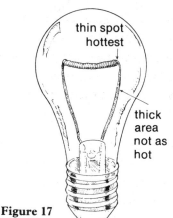

thin spot hottest

thick area not as hot

Figure 17

Some atoms on the surface of the filament vaporize because it is so hot. They change directly from a solid to a gas in the same way that dry ice (frozen carbon dioxide) changes from a solid to a gas. The vaporization of the filament is quite slow, but gradually the filament grows slightly thinner at one place.

It is harder for electric current to go through a thinner wire. The resistance to electric current flow increases. Because it is harder for the current to flow, the current loses more energy in that thin section of the filament. The filament gets hotter where it is thin.

What happens when this thinner section of filament gets hotter? Atoms vaporize from the surface more rapidly and the wire thins more quickly than the surrounding sections of wire, as shown in Figure 17. Because it gets thinner still, the resistance increases and that part of the filament gets hotter. Eventually, the filament gets thin enough to break or melt.

The tops of old light bulbs are often black. This is because the vaporized atoms from the filament rise to the top of the bulb and condense, or turn back into a solid. The tungsten lost from the filament collects at the top of the bulb.

But how are quartz halogen lights different from normal lights? Halogens are reactive gases, like chlorine and fluorine. They undergo chemical reactions quite easily. In a light bulb, they combine with the atoms that have been vaporized from the filament. The halogen that bonds to the tungsten moves around in the light bulb until it touches a hot object—the filament. At that point, it deposits the tungsten and then moves away. More tungsten is given up where the filament is the hottest. (This is also the place where the filament is the thinnest.) The halogen gas literally puts the tungsten back where it is needed the most.

This allows you to have a brighter bulb because the bulb literally repairs itself. It can be burned hotter than normal, which means that it gives off more light. Eventually the filament weakens somewhere and the bulb burns out, but the halogen gas allows the bulb to burn much longer than conventional light bulbs.

You must be careful when installing quartz halogen lights not to touch the glass casing of the bulb. If you touch it with your fingers, you leave a little oil from your fingerprint on the outside of the bulb. When you turn on the bulb, this oil quickly burns and leaves a carbon film. This carbon film heats up because it is black. Instead of having all the tungsten moved back onto the filament, some moves onto the bulb where you touched it. The bulb burns out much faster. It may also burn out because the bulb cracks from the higher temperature.

Review Questions

1) How does a light bulb give off light?

2) Why do the filaments in light bulbs become thinner?

3) What happens to the thin spots along the filament? What results?

4) What happens in halogen lights to make them last longer?

TEACHER

Answers

1) A light bulb gives off light because the electric current flowing in the filament makes it glow white-hot.

2) The filaments become thinner because some atoms are changed directly into a gas. The term for this is *sublimation.* Thinning makes the resistance of that part of the filament become greater, causing a rise in temperature at that point. This makes the atoms vaporize faster and accelerates the thinning rate.

3) The temperature rises because the current loses more energy flowing through an area of more resistance. This makes the thinner area thin faster.

4) The halogen gas literally transports the vaporized filament back to the hottest places on the filament, which happen to be the thinnest places. This slows the thinning process.

The technology of light bulbs is quite old. Edison did a lot of experimentation before he found a filament that worked. His carbon filament has been replaced with tungsten and other combinations of metals, but the problem of preventing the filament from burning out remains the same. Any oxygen will oxidize the filament and cause it to burn out prematurely. Another reason that bulbs burn out is that the filaments break. A hot filament is more brittle than a cold one, so it is easier to burn out a bulb that is burning than one that is not. Bulbs may also burn out when you turn them on because the rapid change in temperature causes the filament to crack. This is why bulbs burn out the moment you turn them on. The filament has thinned to a point where it can't stand the rapid change in temperature.

The vaporization of the filament is a rather long process in most light bulbs, but it is the reason all light bulbs eventually burn out. Long-life bulbs can be made in many different ways, but one way is to make the bulb have less current flow through it. With less current, it does not burn as hot so it lasts longer, but it also doesn't give off as much light. The lower the wattage (or power lost in the light bulb), the longer the bulbs tend to last.

Some light bulbs are made specially for certain uses. Photoflood light bulbs are used for photography and have a higher temperature, which is more like sunlight. These bulbs tend to burn out rapidly.

A possible demonstration for how a light bulb burns out quickly can be done by carefully removing the glass from around a light bulb (see page 60). When you turn on the light, the bulb quickly burns out because of its exposure to oxygen. If you do this experiment, make sure that everyone has proper eye protection or do the experiment behind a transparent shield.

18

How Fluorescent Lights Work

Fluorescent lights are long tubes that glow. Sometimes the tubes are curved into spirals. More recently, they have started to look much like regular incandescent light bulbs. Fluorescent lights are much more efficient than normal light bulbs, which only turn about 5% of their electrical energy into light. How are these lights different from regular lights? How do they work?

Regular light bulbs or incandescent bulbs, work by heating a filament. Electricity gives up its energy as it passes through the filament. The wire gets hot and gives off light. However, most of the energy changes into heat energy, while only a small part is changed into light.

The fluorescent light works in a different way. It has a tube filled with a gas, which includes some mercury vapor. When the light is turned on, electrons move down the tube at great speeds hitting the mercury atoms as they go. The collision of these electrons with the atoms causes electrons in the mercury atoms to be moved to higher energy levels. When the electrons move back down to their normal positions, they give off light.

In fluorescent light bulbs, the mercury atoms give off photons in the ultraviolet part of the spectrum. This light is harmful, but a layer of phosphors is spread on the inside of the glass tube. These phosphors glow

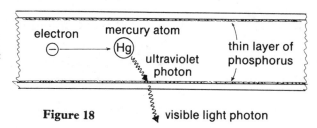

Figure 18

when hit by ultraviolet light and give off white light, as shown in Figure 18.

Review Questions

1) How are incandescent and fluorescent lights different?

2) How is white light made in a fluorescent bulb?

3) Why are fluorescent lights more efficient?

4) How is light given off by the atoms in a fluorescent light?

TEACHER

Answers

1) Incandescent lights use a glowing filament to give off light, while fluorescent lights make a gas glow by sending high-energy electrons through it.

2) The ultraviolet light given off when electrons collide with the mercury gas is changed to white light by phosphors spread on the inside of the glass tube.

3) Fluorescent lights are more efficient because they don't change as much energy to heat.

4) Electrons moving at high speed collide with atoms. Electrons in the atoms are moved up to higher energy levels and when they return to their normal levels, they give off photons.

Fluorescent lights are used in many places because they are much more efficient than incandescent lights. The electrons moving in the tube exchange energy efficiently with the mercury atoms in the gas. The phosphors then change the ultraviolet light into light that is safe and efficient.

The electrons in the tube are accelerated down the tube by high voltage generated by a transformer. This high voltage creates an electric field in the tube. The electrons travel down the tube in fits and starts because they gain energy from the electric field and then lose energy to the atoms of the gas.

Some fluorescent lights need a little time to warm up. Sometimes you have to hold a button to start them because it is difficult for the electrons to begin moving through the gas. Once some electrons have traveled down the tube, they ionize the gas—or make the atoms in the gas charged. Once an ionized pathway forms, the electrons can travel more easily in the gas. The starter gets the charge moving by ionizing the gas for a few moments. Once the gas ionizes, the electrons can move down the tube more easily.

19
Three-Way Light Bulbs

A three-way light bulb is an interesting device that gives three different levels of brightness. You can choose the low setting to save energy or the high setting to make things very bright. But how does this light work? How does one light bulb burn in three different ways?

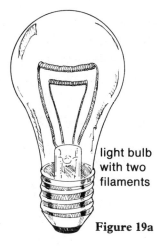

light bulb with two filaments

Figure 19a

A three-way light bulb works because it has two filaments, as shown in Figure 19a. If the bulb can put out 50, 100, and 150 watts, then the filaments are 50 and 100 watts. If you want 50 watts, the switch only lights the 50-watt filament. If you want 100 watts, only the 100-watt one is lit. If you want 150 watts, then both are lit. The switch that operates these lamps is a special one and the bottom of the light bulb is different from the bottom of a normal light bulb.

What happens if you put a regular bulb into a three-way socket? The bulb stays lit for two of the four positions and is out for the other two.

You can observe the differences in these bulbs and see what different connections must be made in the lights to make them work.

WARNING: NEVER use light sockets that are plugged into a source of electricity in any of your investigations.

Use unwired sockets from a hardware store, which can't be plugged into an outlet.

Examine the bases of three-way and regular light bulbs and record the differences. Then examine three-way and regular light sockets. Record these differences. Try to explain which connections must be used when just the regular light bulb is in the socket. Draw diagrams of both types of socket and of the bottoms of both types of bulb.

Review Questions

1) What filaments must be used in a light bulb that can put out 25 watts, 50 watts, and 75 watts?

2) What happens when a regular light bulb is placed in a three-way socket? How does this happen?

3) How must the switch in the socket of a three-way bulb work? What connections must it make, based on the diagram you drew of the bottom of the bulb?

┌─────────────┐
│ **TEACHER** │
└─────────────┘

Materials Needed	
three-way bulbs	cloth
sockets	broom
hammer	dustpan

Answers

1) You would have to use a 25-watt and a 50-watt filament.

2) The bulb is on for two positions of the switch and off for the other two.

3) The switch must be designed so it connects none, one or the other of the filaments, or both of them.

This experiment can be done quite easily and allows students to see how these bulbs work. The best way to do the experiment is to buy some bulbs and sockets at a hardware store. They are relatively inexpensive and can be used again.

> **WARNING:** NEVER use sockets that are plugged in or wired to an electrical circuit.

Students should be reminded that the glass of the bulbs can easily break. You should have the means to clean up broken bulbs. Observing the differences in the bulbs and drawing diagrams should allow students to talk about the differences even when they don't have the bulbs and sockets in front of them.

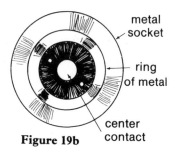

Figure 19b

metal socket

ring of metal

center contact

Students should be able to match up the prongs in the sockets and the metallic screw-in base with the contacts on the light bulb. The part of the base with the screw threads on it makes one contact with the light bulb. In normal bulbs, one other contact is needed. The contacts are insulated from each other. In the three-way bulb, there are two contacts, plus the metal part with screw threads. These are shown in Figure 19b and are similar to what the students should draw.

You may want to carefully remove the glass from a regular bulb and a three-way bulb so students can see the filaments. This can be done carefully with a hammer if the bulb is wrapped in cloth. Be careful not to damage the filaments. You must discard the cloth after use because it is impossible to remove all the small pieces of glass from it. You should also use eye protection and gloves. After breaking the glass, wrap the rough edges with tape so that no small pieces of glass or sharp metal edges are exposed. Students should also be told to look at and not touch the filaments, for they can easily be broken. The filaments can also be seen more readily if clear glass bulbs are used, not frosted or "soft white" bulbs.

20
Electric Motors

Electric motors are useful to us. Small electric motors run watches, while large electric motors move trains. To make a motor turn, a magnetic field must go one way and then the other. This makes the motor turn all the way around.

Many electric motors use a combination of *permanent magnets* and *electro-magnets*. A permanent magnet is often made out of iron and is similar to a horse-shoe magnet. An electromagnet is a coil of wire carrying an electric current. Electromagnets are useful because the magnetic field's direction can be changed by changing the direction in which the current flows in the coil of wire. An iron core may be placed inside the coil to concentrate the magnetic field.

You can make a simple "electric" motor with two bar magnets. Your motor will not really be electric because you will change the direction in which a magnet points instead of changing the direction in which current flows in an electromagnet. But remember, an electric motor just uses electric current to make the field of an electromagnet change direction.

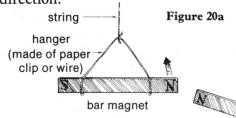

Figure 20a

Hang a bar magnet on a support using a string and a hook made out of a small piece of wire. The magnet should be held horizontally, as shown in Figure 20a. Now hold the north end of another mag-net near the hanging one. The hanging magnet should turn until its south end points toward the magnet you are holding. (Remember, opposite magnetic poles attract and like poles repel.) Once the south end points toward the magnet in your hand, quickly turn your magnet so the south end points toward the hanging magnet. The hanging magnet should keep turning. Continue making the magnet turn by turning your magnet at the appropriate times. The hanging magnet is now a motor. It turns because you keep changing the magnetic field it is in. How fast can you make it spin?

Electric motors work on the same principle. They are different from your motor because they change the magnetic field by making current flow one way and then the other. Your teacher may have some electric motors for you to examine. How are they like the one you built? How are they different?

TEACHER

Materials Needed

bar magnets   wire (paper clips)   nail

string   battery

materials for a commutator or a simple motor

This exercise can be done easily if you have a supply of bar magnets. Each group needs two. Large paper clips can be unbent to form the holder for the magnet. This can be connected to the support with a string.

Students may have a little trouble initially with getting the timing right for making the motor spin. If they are having trouble, emphasize the reason the motor turns. It turns because of opposite-pole attraction and like-pole repulsion. The hanging magnet is initially attracted to the one held in the hand. However, to keep it spinning, the magnet held in the hand must be turned once the opposite poles are together to create opposite-pole repulsion. If you don't turn the hand-held magnet, the hanging magnet will stop turning.

Students may find it fun if you hold a competition to see which group can make the hanging magnet spin fastest. You can do this by counting the number of times the magnet spins in 30 seconds.

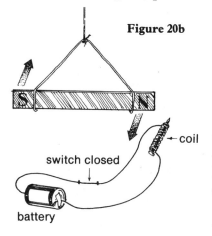

Figure 20b

This motor may not satisfy some students because it uses no electricity. The principle is the same, but instead of changing the direction of the current with a switch or other means, the students change the field by moving the magnet. You may satisfy these students by making an electromagnet. Wrap a coil of wire around a nail and connect it to a flashlight battery (don't use higher voltage). By switching the current on and off, you can make the coil magnetic and then not. If the coil is held near the hanging magnet and turned on, the hanging magnet will turn toward the coil (see Figure 20b). When it aligns, turn the coil off and let the magnet turn another half turn. Then turn the coil on and attract the hanging magnet again. With proper timing, the hanging magnet will spin. It spins because of electric current. You may even want to have the students make their own coils and run this experiment on their own.

Building a real electric motor takes a bit more effort. If you use safe, low-voltage flashlight batteries, you will need to wind wire on an iron nail to contentrate the field. You then have to build a commutator, which will switch the current in the coil of wire. When this is placed near a fixed magnet, the coil should turn until the magnets are close to each other with opposite-pole attraction. At this point, the commutator should switch the direction of current. It may be possible to borrow a simple motor from a physics teacher for this demonstration rather than build one.

You may also wish to test your bar magnets. Some may be very weak and have no real effect. Some may also have had their poles reversed because they have been near a strong magnet. If the poles are reversed, it confuses the students. The reversed magnets can be corrected if they are brought next to a strong magnet and gently tapped.

21
How Magnetic Tape or Disks Can Store Information

We all are familiar with tape recorders, videotape machines, and computer disks. But how do they work? What allows a magnetic film to save information that can be used at a later time?

Magnetic tapes and disks are made with a thin layer of magnetic particles spread on a film, generally made of plastic. These particles are affected by a magnet. They align along magnetic fields; when the magnetic fields are removed, they stay in their new positions.

When information is put on a magnetic tape, magnetic patterns are made. When the tape or disk goes past the play head, the magnetic patterns cause small currents to flow in the head. These small currents are amplified and either make sound or pictures, or tell a computer the recorded information.

One danger with any magnetic recording is that if a magnet comes near it, the information is lost. The magnet rearranges the magnetic particles on the tape or disk. People who regularly use magnets, such as science teachers, may have problems if they carry credit cards in a wallet. Most credit cards contain information stored on a magnetic strip. Moving the magnet too close to the wallet causes all the information on the magnetic strip to be lost.

It is possible to make patterns similar to those formed by magnets on the magnetic tape. You need iron filings, a piece of stiff cardboard, and a strong magnet. A one-foot square piece of cardboard is large enough to show the effect.

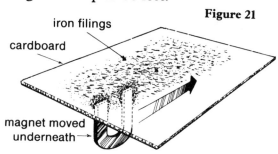

Figure 21

iron filings
cardboard
magnet moved underneath

Sprinkle some iron filings on top of the cardboard, as shown in Figure 21. Move the magnet underneath from one end to the other. If the magnet is close to the cardboard, you should see patterns formed, which remain after the magnet is removed. See what kinds of patterns you can make. Have someone make a pattern and then see if you can figure out what he or she did to make the pattern. What kind of patterns do you get if you move the cardboard while keeping the magnet stationary? Why might this be so?

How Everyday Things Work

TEACHER

Materials Needed		
iron filings	strong magnets	cardboard

The technology for storing information in the magnetic medium is really quite amazing. The magnetic fields that are left on the tape or disk are very small, but they are positioned there very precisely. The tape head or the disk head moves over these patterns to retrieve the information.

Small coils of wire are used to put the information on the magnetic film and to retrieve it. The coil of wire becomes a magnet when current flows in it. Different patterns can be made by varying the amount of current flowing through the coil as the magnetic film moves past the record head. The information is also retrieved using a coil of wire. As the changing magnetic fields move past the coil, they cause small currents to flow in the play head coil. (A current flows to oppose a change of magnetic field in a coil of wire.) These small currents are amplified and the information on the tape or disk can then be used.

This experiment is rather simple and the results will be clear if you use relatively strong magnets. Make sure to test the magnets before you run the lab. If they are weak, you and your students will be frustrated. You may also be able to find some magnetic toys that work using the same basic process.

Students should be encouraged to try to make as many different kinds of patterns as they can. Swirls can be made if the magnet is spun under the cardboard. Have students avoid getting iron filings on their magnets, as they are quite hard to remove.

Either the magnet or the cardboard may be moved. Only the relative motion is important. Students should try to make patterns as they move the cardboard, because this is the way patterns are made on the tape.

You might try setting up an electromagnet in which you can vary its field (you will need a variable voltage supply). By changing the voltage that produces the magnetic field, you will be able to model more closely the way these recording devices work.

22
How Does a TV Make a Picture?

How does a picture form on a television screen? What steps are needed and what scientific principles are behind them? Basically, information to make a picture is picked up by the TV antenna. It is sent to the TV along antenna wires and tells devices inside the TV which parts of the screen to light up and which to leave dark. The antenna also receives information to make the sound.

Let us first think about a black and white TV because it is a bit simpler. Inside the television is a picture tube that is flat on one end where the screen is and has a cylinder at the other. The tube contains what is called an *electron gun,* which "fires" electrons at the screen end of the cylinder.

An electron gun is actually rather simple. A wire is made red-hot by sending current through it, similar to the way a light bulb is made to light. When the wire is this hot, the atoms in the wire move very rapidly and some

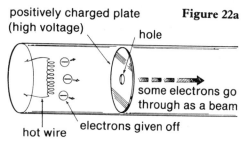

Figure 22a

positively charged plate (high voltage) — hole — some electrons go through as a beam — hot wire — electrons given off

electrons are knocked off the wire. Electrons are negatively charged. A positively charged plate attracts the electrons because opposite charges attract. The plate has a small hole in it and some of the electrons pass through the hole instead of hitting the plate. The electrons going through the hole form the beam of electrons that is fired at the screen, as shown in Figure 22a. As the electrons move toward the positive plate, they move faster—about one-tenth the speed of light.

The narrow beam of electrons that has passed through the plate holes then passes close to coils of wire, as shown in Figure 22b. The coils of wire are electromagnets that carry current. Magnetic fields exert forces on moving charged particles like electrons. The coils of wire change the direction of the electrons in the beam. Electrons are directed either up or down or to the right or

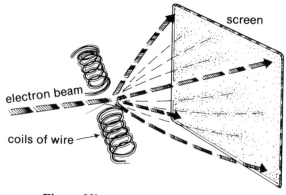

screen — electron beam — coils of wire

Figure 22b

left, depending on how the current moves in the coils. This means that the coils direct the electron beam to different parts of the screen.

To make a picture on the screen, the beam is directed so that it starts in the top corner and then moves horizontally across the screen. When the beam reaches the other side, the beam is returned to its starting position, except that it has moved down one line. The electron beam travels across the screen 525 times to make a picture.

In order to make black and white areas on the screen, the electron beam is turned on or off. If a particular spot on the screen is to be light, the beam is turned on; if it is to be dark, the beam is turned off. Information picked up by the antenna tells the electron gun either to fire or not to fire, thereby turning the beam on or off. When electrons strike the screen, they cause phosphors on the screen to "phosphoresce," or give off light. The energy of the electron beam is turned into light.

A color TV is similar to the black and white TV. American sets use three electron guns instead of one. Each gun is aimed at phosphors that glow in the three primary colors. As these colored phosphors give off light, the color picture is formed.

The phosphors are chosen to give off light only briefly, so that the picture can keep changing. If they gave off light for a long time after being struck by the electrons, then you could not get a new picture. A new picture is produced in $\frac{1}{30}$ of a second, so the picture is changed very rapidly. This makes motion on the screen seem smooth.

Review Questions

1) What is an electron gun and how does it fire electrons at the screen?

2) How are the electrons directed at different parts of the screen?

3) How are different parts of the screen made either bright or dark?

4) How is a color TV different from a black and white one?

5) What is the purpose of phosphors in a TV? What properties must they have? Why?

TEACHER

Answers

1) The electron gun gets a supply of electrons from a hot wire because the thermal motion knocks them free of atoms. These negative electrons are accelerated because they are attracted toward a positive plate with a hole in it. Some of the electrons go through the hole and form a narrow beam.

2) Electrons are directed at different parts of the screen by magnetic fields produced in coils of wire. (The strength of the magnetic field depends on how much current flows through the wires; the stronger the magnetic field, the more the electron beam is deflected.) By using coils above and below and on the right and left of the beam, the beam can be directed to all parts of the screen.

3) The beam is switched on and off by the information picked up by the antenna. If the information the antenna picks up is distorted because of an airplane or other disturbance, ghost images may be seen on the screen because the reflected TV waves may tell the gun to fire at the wrong time. If the station is far away and the signal is weak, the electron gun may not fire at the appropriate times and there will be static or snow on the screen.

4) Three electron guns fire at slightly different angles in a color TV. The beams go through a metal screen that allows only one gun to hit a particular color phosphor. The alignment of the screen, the guns, and the cost of the colored phosphors make color TVs more expensive to make.

5) The phosphors light up to create the visual image. Some places are not lit up, so the screen appears dark at that spot. The phosphors stop glowing quickly so action is not blurred.

The television takes advantage of some basic physics in that the motion of electrons in electric fields shows how opposites are attracted. The electrons have a force exerted on them over a distance and they gain energy. The electron energy is related to the voltage between the hot wire and the positive plate. More energy is gained by the electrons when they go through high voltages than through low voltages.

The forces on the electron beam are produced by magnets, according to what is known as the *left-hand rule*. Hold out your left hand. If the motion of the electrons points in the direction of your thumb and the magnetic field points in the direction of your outstretched fingers, the force on the electrons (negative charges) is in the direction which your palm would push up. See Figure 22c. (Note: this is opposite the direction in which positive charges move. Forces on positive charges can be found in a similar manner using the right hand instead of the left.)

TV's use high voltage to accelerate the electrons because the electrons must have enough energy to excite the phosphors and travel as a coherent beam. The voltages are typically near 10,000 volts.

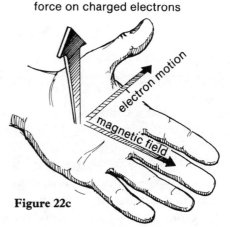

force on charged electrons

electron motion

magnetic field

Figure 22c

WARNING: This is why it is dangerous to open the back of a television. This voltage can kill a person very easily. Because there are capacitors, devices which store charge, this high voltage may be present long after the TV is unplugged. Students should be reminded that they should **never** open the back of the TV to investigate what is in there.

23

How Sound Travels Over a Lake

On a calm evening on a pond or lake, you can often hear voices coming from distant places. How often does this happen and what causes it?

The sounds you hear are sound waves that travel through the air. The source of sound compresses some air molecules. These molecules expand and compress the next group of air molecules, which expand and compress the next group, etc. The rate at which the wave moves is called the *speed of sound*. It depends on how fast a group of molecules expands into the next. This speed is related to the temperature. Molecules in gas move faster at higher temperatures. The speed of sound is 331 m/sec at 0°C and increases .6 m/sec for every 1°C rise in temperature.

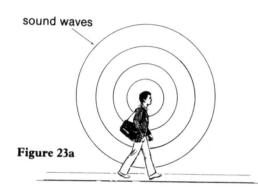

sound waves

Figure 23a

Sound, like most waves, normally travels in straight lines and in all directions, as shown in Figure 23a. Because sound goes in so many directions, the energy of the wave spreads out quickly. However, on a calm evening on a lake, this spreading does not always happen. This is because the water cools the air directly above the lake faster than the air higher up. This makes a layer of cool air near the lake, with warmer air above it, as shown in Figure 23b.

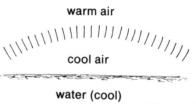

warm air

cool air

water (cool)

Figure 23b

This temperature difference causes the sound to stay near the lake's surface. A sound wave from someone speaking would not normally reach you. However, because of the different temperature of air over the lake it is bent, or *refracted*, to your ears.

But what is refraction and how does it occur? Imagine the sound waves as a series of lines, as shown in Figure 23b. These lines show the compressions of waves as they move in the air. The top part of a sound wave moves faster than its bottom

How Everyday Things Work

part as it starts upward. (The speed of sound is faster in the warmer air.) Because the top moves faster than the bottom, it makes the wave change direction. It starts going up, then moves horizontally, and finally moves down. This bending is called refraction.

Refraction allows you to hear voices at great distances. The sound energy doesn't rise up above the lake, it is bent back down. The result is more sound energy comes to your ears so you can hear more easily. When the sound travels very long distances, it may bounce off the surface of the lake and then refract back down again off the warm air, as shown in Figure 23c. The sound literally bounces or skips across the lake!

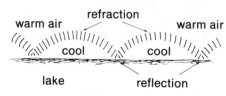

Figure 23c

Other interesting things happen because of refraction of sound waves. Normally when thunderstorms occur, the air is warm near the ground and cool higher up, the opposite of what happened on the lake. When thunder occurs, the sounds tend to bend upward because sound travels faster near the ground, as shown in Figure 23d. For this reason, thunder cannot be heard at distances greater than about 10 miles. The sound is refracted, or bent, over your head.

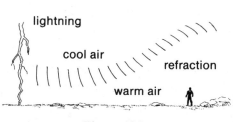

Figure 23d

An interesting example of refracted sound waves occurred one spring along the coast of New Jersey. Loud booms coming from over the ocean kept being heard. For a while, no one could figure out what was happening and some people became quite scared. It turned out that it was just refraction of sound waves. The booms were caused by jet fighters far off the coast practicing for battle. The jets were flying faster than the speed of sound, so they made sonic booms. Normally, these sounds would not even come close to the shore, but there was a strange weather pattern occurring. A layer of cold air was sandwiched between two warmer layers of air, as shown in Figure 23e. When the planes flew through this layer, the booms were heard.

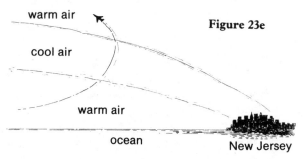

Figure 23e

Think about why this happened, based on what you have read about thunder and about sounds traveling over a lake.

Review Questions

1) What determines the speed of sound in air?

2) Why can sounds be heard long distances over a lake when it is calm?

3) Why can't thunder be heard at great distances?

4) Can you explain how the sonic booms of jets reached the New Jersey coast?

Teacher

Answers

1) The speed of sound is determined by the average speed of the molecules. At higher temperatures, the speed is greater.

2) Because the air is warmer above the lake than at the lake's surface, sound refracts back down to the lake. The energy doesn't spread out as fast so it can be heard at a greater distance.

3) Because the air is warmer near the ground, the sound refracts up over your head.

4) The cool air acted as a sound pathway. With warmer air above and below, sound refracted so it stayed in the cool air. It refracted up if it was headed down and refracted down if it was headed up.

The refraction of sound waves often seems mysterious to people but actually is quite a common phenomenon. The analysis of the bending of the waves is quite easy if done in the way described in the student section. Understanding how the waves will bend helps to explain many things.

It may be helpful to draw a diagram on the board to help the students see how the bending occurs. Draw a diagram similar to Figure 23b. Put your hand parallel to the wave as it goes upward. If your fingers are up in the warm air, they move faster than the heel of your hand. By drawing attention to why you are moving your fingers faster than the heel of your hand, students generally can see why the wave comes back down. A similar diagram can be drawn to show why sounds waves bend upward when the air is cooler higher up.

The booms coming in over the New Jersey coast caused quite a bit of excitement. Concerned people put forth many different theories. However, the discovery of the cool layer of air that met the shoreline made it easy to explain. Sound was trapped in the cool layer because if the sound moved either up or down, refraction would bring it back into the cool layer. The cool layer acted as a path for the sound and the warm layers acted as "shepherds," keeping the sound waves in line.

24

How You Hear

Hearing is a wonderful sense for those who are blessed with it. But how does a sound wave make an impression on the brain? What goes on between the source of sound and our hearing?

Sound is a wave that moves through a *medium*. A medium can be any substance. Sound travels well in water or steel and can often be heard at great distances in these media. A wave travels because a section of the medium is compressed and the compressed section expands into the next section of the medium. This compresses the next section so it expands into the next section, etc.

When a tree falls and hits the ground, it compresses air and starts a sound wave. The sound wave then travels away from the falling tree as one section of

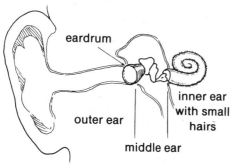

Figure 24a

eardrum

inner ear with small hairs

outer ear

middle ear

air expands and compresses the next. When the sound wave reaches your eardrum through the outer ear, it pushes on the eardrum so the eardrum moves. The eardrum causes the bones in your ear (the *anvil*, the *hammer,* and the *stirrup*) to move. These bones transfer the motion of the eardrum through the *middle ear* to the *inner ear*. The bones amplify the motion of the eardrum and make it easier for the inner ear to function, as shown in Figure 24a.

The inner ear is filled with fluid and is shaped like a curled-up horn. It is wider next to the middle ear and gets smaller farther away. Inside the inner ear are thousands of tiny hairs. Each hair is attached to a nerve which sends information to the brain.

When the bones of the middle ear push on the inner ear, the fluid in it moves. Sound is made up of different *frequencies,* or rates of vibration. These different frequencies cause certain hairs in the middle ear to vibrate. Each hair vibrates at its own frequency. If a particular hair vibrates, you hear that frequency.

But why do particular hairs vibrate at their own frequencies? The reason is that the hairs are all different lengths. In the same way that a xylophone has different length bars to make different frequencies or pitched notes, the hairs in your inner ear are different lengths in order to hear different notes. Objects tend to vibrate at various rates, depending on their size. Short objects tend to vibrate at high frequencies and longer objects at lower frequencies. You can demonstrate this if you take a meterstick and press down on it when most of it is off the edge of a table. When you lift one end and let it go, it slowly vibrates up and down. If you move the stick so less is off the edge of the table, then the vibration is much faster.

Just as vibrating things give off sounds, sounds can cause things to vibrate. A guitar string vibrates at a certain pitch when plucked. However, if you play a note of the same frequency from a speaker, the string vibrates even though you don't touch it. If the frequency is not the same, nothing happens. This is the case with the hairs in your inner ear. Each hair vibrates at a different frequency.

When a hair vibrates, the nerve attached to it fires. This sends a signal to the brain. The brain then processes this information and you hear. The processing of information is complex and is not completely understood. We know that sometimes the process can be confused and people have hearing loss related to the processing of information rather than to any of the mechanical functions that go on in the ear.

Hearing loss can also occur for other reasons. If the eardrum is broken, you lose hearing in that ear. The eardrum can be broken by explosions, such as fireworks let off too close to the ear. The middle ear can be damaged by infections and the hairs of the inner ear can be damaged if they are exposed to loud noises. The louder the sound and the longer one is exposed to it, the more damage occurs.

WARNING: BEWARE, loud noises can be dangerous to your hearing.

Review Questions

1) What are sound waves and how do they travel?

2) How do each of the parts of the ear help us to hear?

3) Why do particular hairs in the inner ear vibrate?

4) What are possible ways to damage hearing?

TEACHER

Answers

1) Sound waves are compressional waves; one section of the medium compresses the next section of the medium, etc.

2) The outer ear collects sound and causes the eardrum to vibrate. The middle ear's bones amplify the motion and transfer the vibrations to the inner ear. The inner ear has many hairs that vibrate at characteristic frequencies. If a particular hair vibrates, that frequency of sound is heard. The vibrating hairs cause nerves to fire and send information to the brain where that information is processed.

3) Hairs of different lengths vibrate at different frequencies.

4) Loud noises can break the eardrum, infections can injure the bones of the middle ear, loud or sustained noises can damage the individual hairs in the inner ear, and the processing of information can be confused.

Hearing is complex, but a general outline can be made using simple principles. Sound is normally defined as the range of frequencies to which the human ear is sensitive. These frequencies range from 20 to 20,000 cycles per second. People lose the ability to hear higher frequencies as the result of aging or of loud noises. People who play in rock bands often have hearing loss and cannot hear frequencies higher than 10,000 cycles per second. This is unfortunate because the high frequencies are in the consonant sounds *p, t, b,* etc.

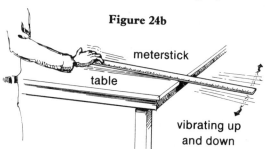

Figure 24b

meterstick

table

vibrating up and down

The demonstration with the meterstick is quick and convincing. If the meterstick is moved so that less and less is hanging off the table, as shown in Figure 24b, the pitch or frequency of vibration rises. You can do this as a demonstration or you can attempt to get the class to play a tune using a number of metersticks to form a scale.

The outer ear functions as a collection device to funnel sound to the eardrum, as well as protecting the eardrum from danger. The middle ear can be damaged by infection and this is one reason doctors are worried about ear infections. Hearing loss due to this source can be prevented. The inner ear is where the sound waves are transferred into nerve impulses. The hairs vibrate at characteristic frequencies determined by their lengths.

25

What Causes Thunder?

Everyone knows that thunder is produced by lightning but not everyone knows why the thunder actually occurs. What makes the loud noise and why do you often hear rumbling?

Lightning is a large spark moving between one cloud and another or between a cloud and the ground. The electric charges moving in the spark have lots of energy. If all the energy of the lightning bolt were used to lift a small car, the car would be lifted half a mile (1 km) into the air.

When the spark jumps, charges move through the air. These moving charges heat up the air to very high temperatures. It is actually hard to measure precisely, but the temperature rises to about 20,000°C. At this temperature, the air molecules glow and give off light. This is the flash of lightning.

Lightning heats the air very rapidly, in less than a tenth of a second. This heated air behaves like any heated gas: it expands. Because the heating is so rapid and to such a high temperature, the air expands violently outward. The expansion occurs all along the lightning bolt so it is like a cylinder of expanding air.

Sound, by definition, is compressional waves that travel through the air. The expanding heated air compresses the air immediately around it and the sound travels outward. The sound is **not** caused by the air coming back together like a clap. The cooling of the air takes place more slowly so it doesn't produce a loud noise.

If you are standing near where the lightning strikes, you generally hear one loud noise. If you are farther away, you hear rumbling. The rumbling is caused by the sound from various parts of the lightning bolt taking different paths to your ears. The sound waves can reflect off hills or mountains or even clouds. Because the sound can come by places and routes of different lengths, sound arrives at separate times, as shown in Figure 25 on page 78.

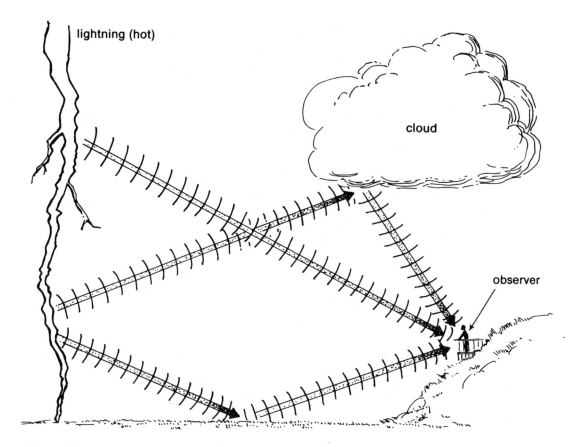

Figure 25   three different paths for sound

Review Questions

1) What is lightning?

2) What is a sound wave and how does lightning produce it?

3) Why does thunder often rumble rather than give one loud noise?

78   *How Everyday Things Work*

TEACHER

Answers

1) Lightning is a large spark going between clouds or a cloud and the ground. A more complete discussion of lightning is given in unit 13, pages 37–41.

2) Sound waves occur because air is compressed. Sound travels as one section of the medium expands into the next section of medium and compresses it. That section expands into the next section, etc. Because of the rapid heating of the air by lightning, the air expands and produces a loud sound wave.

3) Thunder can echo off clouds, hills, and mountains. For this reason, even though the thunder is started during a very brief period, it may last for many seconds.

Most people have experienced thunder. The theory is not complete because neither the temperature of the lightning bolt nor the exact manner of heating the air are precisely known. However, the general theory seems correct.

The expansion of the heated gas actually produces what is called a *shock wave*. A shock wave occurs when the expansion is faster than the speed of sound. The expansion literally moves faster than the speed at which the air molecules can move out of the way because of the intense heating. After a brief time, the expansion slows to below the speed of sound and then the sound travels like a normal sound wave.

The shape of the shock wave determines how the sound travels. Because the shock wave is like a cylinder around the lightning bolt, the sound is louder for those who are perpendicular to the bolt than for for those who are parallel to it. If the bolt hits a lightning rod on the roof of a house, the sound may not be very loud in the house. It tends to be a sharp crack instead of a boom.

Other noises are associated with lightning strikes. The air may literally crackle or hiss as smaller electric discharges occur. Metal objects may buzz or vibrate. Sometimes a crack is heard and this may be associated with positive charges from the ground meeting the negative charges coming from the cloud.

Thunder cannot be heard at distances greater than 10 to 15 miles because sound rises. During thunderstorms, the air is warmer near the ground. Under these conditions, the sound refracts upward and cannot be heard far away. This is why it is possible to see lightning from a distant storm and not hear any thunder. People often call this "heat lightning." (See unit 23, pages 70–73.)

26

How Stringed Instruments Play Different Notes

When you play a stringed instrument, you make sound waves. These waves are caused by other waves that are made in the string. You can learn more about waves by looking at the waves in the string.

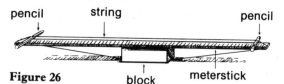

Figure 26

You'll need a stringed instrument. You could make a simple one, as shown in Figure 26, or you could use a violin or guitar. Pluck the string gently and observe the way the string vibrates. Make sure the string doesn't move at the ends. Describe how the string moves and what it looks like.

Now, pluck the string and listen to the pitch it makes. You may have to move your ear close to the string to hear it. Now, pluck the string when you have a finger placed 10 cm from one end of the string. What changes do you see in the way the string vibrates? What changes do you hear?

Can you play different notes? Start by playing the lowest note, without touching the string. Then place a finger near one of the ends, pressing firmly. Pluck the string and listen to the sound. Move your finger farther from the end and try to make the notes of the scale.

Waves are created by vibrations. The sound waves you hear are caused by the vibrations in the string. The vibration goes up and down the string at approximately the same velocity regardless of the string's length. If it has a shorter distance to go, the wave is shorter. With a shorter distance to go, it vibrates faster. Does this agree with what you observed about the string's length and pitch? (Higher pitch means higher frequency vibration.)

One octave is a whole scale: do, re, mi . . . do. What do you have to do to go from low "do" to high "do"? What happens to the length of the string to make this change? How does the time it takes for the wave to travel up and down the string change?

If waves in strings are similar to sound waves, how does the wavelength seem to relate to frequency and pitch? How do you move your finger to change the pitch one octave? What must this mean about the frequency of the sound? Record your observations.

How Everyday Things Work

TEACHER

Materials Needed

stringed instruments

or

pencils	tape	string
metersticks		blocks

You will need stringed instruments for this exercise. You may either borrow them or have the students construct their own using metersticks, pencils, tape, string, and blocks, as shown in Figure 26 on page 80.

To make this simple stringed instrument, the string needs to be relatively strong and lightweight. Fishing line works well. The string should be a little more than 2 m long. Tie the string around the meterstick as tightly as you can. Then push a pencil under the string at each end, perpendicular to the meterstick, and tape the pencils in place. The string should now vibrate. If it is not tight enough to vibrate and make a sound, tighten the string. Perhaps you will need to use a wood block or other material, as shown in Figure 26 on page 80. It will speed things up if you have these built in advance but it is possible for students to build them. They may have trouble getting enough tension in the string.

Students should initially observe that the string moves from side to side or up and down. The actual shape is half of a sine wave. The string will have a particular pitch and when the length is shortened, the pitch will be higher. The half-sine wave will be shorter and the wavelength will be smaller. If a finger is placed on the middle of the string, the wave is half as long. Therefore, the frequency is twice as high, which corresponds to an octave.

Students should try to relate the length of the wave in the string to the pitch they hear. As the string is made shorter, the wave in the string travels back and forth faster because it travels a shorter distance. This causes the string to vibrate faster and give a higher pitch. The wave speed is the same because the tension is about the same in the string. Because sound waves are like the waves in the string, when the wavelength is halved, the frequency is doubled.

You may want to encourage students to play tunes on their instruments for fun.

How Putting Your Ear to the Ground Helps You Hear

Oh, those Indian scouts were wise. They could put an ear to the ground and tell you someone was coming on horseback. Is it possible? Yes, but how does it work?

The scouts were able to hear the sound of animal hooves pounding directly on the ground. When a hoof meets the ground, we hear a sound if we are standing nearby. The vibration that occurs as the foot hits the ground causes air molecules to vibrate. These vibrations travel to our ears through the air as sound.

However, we might not be able to hear the sound of the hoof at a distance, perhaps because of obstacles. A house or a hill may make it difficult for the sound waves to reach our ears. Sound waves, like other waves, can bend around corners (in what is called diffraction) but the result is never as loud as hearing the sound directly.

Figure 27

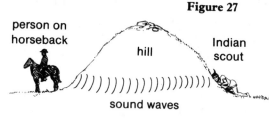

person on horseback
hill
Indian scout
sound waves

When you put your ear to the ground, sound waves come directly to your ear from the point where they were produced. These vibrations travel through rock or ground, as shown in Figure 27. The vibration moves in the ground in the same way as sound waves move in the air. In air, one section of air is compressed, which then expands and compresses the next section of air. The same thing occurs in rock: one section of rock is compressed, which expands and compresses the next section of rock, etc.

If there are pounding hooves on the other side of a hill, their sound comes directly through the rock to the Indian scout's ear. This sound doesn't have to go around obstacles. The scout wouldn't be able to hear speech, because sound doesn't easily travel from the air into the ground. Since the hooves pound

How Everyday Things Work

directly on the ground, the sound enters the rock. You may have experienced something similar while swimming. You might recall that you can hear sounds when you are in the water. The noise made by boat propellers is easy to hear because the propellers are in the water, but voices are seldom heard. Sounds traveling in air don't move easily into water.

Review Questions

1) Why can you sometimes hear distant sounds through the ground although you can't hear them through the air?

2) Why could scouts hear horse hooves but not voices?

3) What sounds can you hear under water and why?

$$\boxed{\textbf{Teacher}}$$

Answers

1) The sound waves come directly to your ear rather than having to go around obstacles. Of course, this works for sound traveling through a hill, but not for sounds traveling across a valley where they travel more directly in the air.

2) The hooves pound directly on the ground so sound waves enter the ground at its source. The sounds of voices are made above the ground and must enter the ground, which is an inefficient process. Much of the sound energy reflects off the ground and doesn't enter it.

3) Sounds produced in the water can be heard easily, while ones out of the water are hard to hear.

It is true that you can hear noises by putting your ear to the ground, but the scouts were taking advantage of some characteristics of the American West. The West often has thin, rocky soil and when a hoof comes down on it, the sound is easily transferred to the bedrock. Likewise, frequent bare rock out-crops allowed the scouts to get in direct touch with the bedrock. This is not true where soils are softer, because the soft soils absorb much of the sound energy.

This section attempts to show that sound waves can travel in other media besides air. Students may remember that they have heard noises under water and this may give them the idea that they can hear noises through solids, too. Some may have tried the somewhat dangerous experiment of putting an ear to the railroad track to hear if a train is coming. Sound can travel through the rails for a few miles, especially with welded track. The activity should be discour-aged because of the danger of being run over by a train.

Sound waves travel around obstacles because of diffraction. Diffraction occurs because each point on the wave can be thought of as a new source of the wave. If the sound wave comes to the edge of a building, the compressed air (which is the sound wave) expands forward but also around the building. As you can imagine, the energy that goes around the building is less than the energy that goes straight. Therefore, when sound diffracts, it becomes softer.

Sound waves also tend to rise because of refraction. When the air is warmer near the ground than higher up (which is often the case during the day), the wave bends upward over the head of a listener. This occurs because sound travels faster in warm air than in cool. The wave near the ground travels faster than the wave higher up so it bends upward. Again, the sound of the horse hooves may not reach the scout's ears through the air.

28

How Your Voice Changes When You Inhale Helium

People sometimes inhale helium and then try to talk. Their voices sound funny because of the way the sound waves are made in the throat and mouth.

WARNING: It is not dangerous to take one breath of helium as long as you breathe in air immediately afterwards. **Never** use any other gases because they can cause explosions or death.

Your voice becomes high-pitched because the speed of sound in helium is faster than the speed of sound in air. But why is there a difference in the speed of sound and why should this make a difference in the way your voice sounds?

The speed of sound in a gas is related to how quickly the gas molecules are moving. The speed at which molecules move is related to their mass and how much energy they have. Warm air molecules have more energy than cold so they move faster. The faster they are moving, the faster sound travels. Sound travels faster in warm air than in cold air.

Helium atoms have much less mass than air molecules. In order for them to have the same amount of energy as an air molecule at room temperature, they must move much faster. This might be compared to the fact that a Ping-Pong ball has to be going much faster than a golf ball to hurt you. Therefore, helium molecules travel faster than air molecules at a given temperature. Likewise, sound waves travel faster in helium than in air.

When you speak, waves resonate in your throat and mouth, as shown in Figure 28. This is similar to the way sounds are made in a wind instrument. A longer tube makes a lower note because it takes longer for the wave to travel the length of the tube. Because sound travels faster in helium than in air, the time it takes for a sound wave to go the length of the throat and mouth is less. The vibration of air in the throat and mouth is therefore faster so the pitch is higher. When your voice is higher-pitched, it sounds strange.

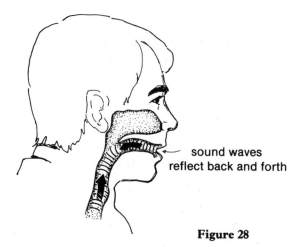

sound waves reflect back and forth

Figure 28

Review Questions

1) What determines the speed of sound in a gas?

2) Why is the speed of sound faster in helium than in air?

3) Why does a higher pitched sound occur as you speak if you have inhaled helium?

TEACHER

Answers

1) The speed of sound is determined by the temperature (which is related to the kinetic energy) and the mass of the molecule.

2) A helium atom has a much lower mass than an air molecule, so to have the same kinetic energy it must be going much faster.

3) In the same way that sound is produced in a wind instrument, sounds are made in the mouth and throat. With a higher speed of sound, it takes a shorter amount of time for the sound waves to move back and forth in the throat and mouth, so higher pitched sounds are produced.

Inhaling helium is safe if done just for one breath. **Inhaling gases other than air is very dangerous.** Make sure that you stress this point.

The speed of sound in helium is actually 981 m/sec at 0°C, whereas it is 343 m/sec in air. This difference in speed makes the frequency of the voice in helium approximately three times the frequency in air. Of course, some air is mixed with the helium so the speed is not changed as much as in pure helium.

The speed of sound is approximated by the average speed of the molecules divided by the square root of 2. The velocity of helium molecules at room temperature can be calculated using the kinetic theory.

Sound is created in the throat and mouth as a standing wave. A standing wave is made as the wave echoes back and forth in the cavity. Some of the wave is reflected at each end, and waves of some frequencies add together to make a large amplitude wave. Other frequencies don't add together so they are not heard. The actual pitch is determined by a number of factors, but the length of the tube is important. Large people tend to have lower voices, because they often have bigger, longer voice boxes.

Some physicists have suggested that another factor plays a part in the change of pitch. They suggest that the vibrations are faster because the helium has less mass. With less mass to move, the vocal chords move faster. Because we are not used to moving less mass, we do not correct for it by reducing the tension on the vocal chords, so the pitch is higher.

29

How a Stereo Speaker Works

A speaker is interesting because it makes sound from electricity. How does it do this? What allows us to hear the electric current?

Figure 29a

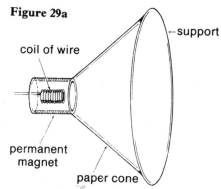

A speaker basically consists of a coil of wire and a magnet. Attached to the coil is some paper. These things are placed in a box. The coil of wire becomes an electromagnet when a current passes through it. Because the electromagnet is near a permanent magnet, it is attracted or repelled when current flows one way and then the other, as shown in Figure 29a. The paper helps amplify the sound.

Sound waves in air are started when the air is compressed. The waves travel because the area of compressed air expands into the next section of air and compresses that section. This next section of air expands, which compresses the next section, etc. You hear the sound when the air finally expands and pushes against your eardrum.

The speaker makes a noise, or starts a sound wave, because the paper attached to the coil moves. Generally, the coil is at the center of a larger ring. The paper joins the coil to the outer ring. When the coil moves in or out, the paper moves. The paper joining the coil to the ring increases the amount of air moved.

But why is something like paper used in speakers? The reason is that the speaker vibrates very rapidly. If a heavy material were used, the coil would have to accelerate a heavier object, which would take more force. This would require a larger coil (which has more mass) or a larger permanent magnet, which is more expensive.

In order for the speaker to make sound, the amplifier sends a varying current to the speaker. If a single note were being played, it would look like a sine wave, as shown in Figure 29b. When many notes are played at the same time, the wave

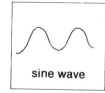

sine wave

Figure 29b

How Everyday Things Work

Figure 29c

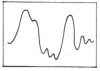

wave of multiple notes being played

looks more complex, as shown in Figure 29c. The sound produced by the speaker resembles this "current wave" because the coil moves in and out depending on how the current moves through the coil.

When the current flows through the coil, it makes the speaker move in (attracted to the permanent magnet) or move out (repelled by the permanent magnet). This occurs because of unlike-pole attraction or like-pole repulsion. The paper brings the coil back to the middle when no current flows. When you look at stereo speakers, you often find there is more than one "speaker" in the box. This is because different sizes work better for different notes. High frequencies, or high notes, are usually produced by a small speaker. The high-frequency speaker may be 5 to 8 cm (2 to 3 in) across. A small speaker is used because the speaker must move in and out very rapidly. The larger the speaker, the more mass must be moved. This makes it harder to build the speaker. The low frequencies are produced by larger speakers. These are used because it is harder to generate low-frequency sounds than high frequencies. You must move more air and move it farther in order to produce loud sounds. Because the frequency is lower, the speaker doesn't have to vibrate as quickly. Large permanent magnets must be used to make the speaker sound properly. With more mass in the larger speaker, more force is needed to make the speaker move in and out.

The box in which the speaker sits is in some ways just decorative, but it is also built to help make sounds rather than hinder making them. It is solidly made so nothing rattles. Sound-absorbing materials are placed in some areas of the box so unwanted vibrations don't occur. In other places, the box is made so it reflects sounds. Acoustical engineers, the people who design speakers, have a challenging job. It is easy to make a simple speaker that sounds acceptable, but harder to make one that reproduces sounds perfectly.

Review Questions

1) What are the main parts of a stereo speaker?

2) How does the speaker produce sound?

3) Why are small speakers used for high pitches and large ones for low pitches?

4) What does the box that holds the speakers do?

$$\boxed{\textbf{T}\text{EACHER}}$$

Answers

1) A speaker is made with a permanent magnet, a coil of wire attached to the rest of the speaker with paper, and a box to hold it.

2) The speaker vibrates as current flows in the electromagnet. If the current flows one way, the magnets attract; if it flows the other way, they are repelled.

3) Small speakers are used to make high frequencies because there is less mass to accelerate. The vibrations can be produced with less current and smaller magnets. Larger forces are needed to accelerate larger masses (f = ma). Larger speakers are needed for low pitches because low-pitched sounds are harder to produce and need a larger vibrating surface.

4) The box that holds the speakers is designed to look nice, not rattle, and hold the speakers in place.

Speaker design for high-quality sound systems is quite complex. The size, the position, and the materials speakers are made from all make a difference in the quality of the sound produced. The basic design of most speakers is the same, however, with a coil and magnet causing vibrations when current flows through the coil. Other kinds of speakers are also produced. One kind is called an *electrostatic speaker,* in which electric forces cause a thin film to vibrate for much the same reason that electrostatic forces hold a balloon against the wall that has been rubbed on your head.

In all speaker designs, there are trade-offs. These occur because of Newton's Law which states that an object in motion tends to stay in motion. In order to make sound, something must move in and out. To move something in and out, forces must be exerted on the mass. The larger the mass, the larger the forces required. With high-frequency sounds especially, small mass is required because the speaker has to vibrate at rates up to 20,000 cycles per second (hertz). With such a high vibration rate, the paper cone of the speaker moves in and out with big accelerations that require large amounts of force.

Large forces on speakers are produced by either increasing the strength of the magnets or making the coil larger. The problem with stronger magnets is cost, while the problem with making the coil larger is that it is then harder to have good frequency response. Once you get current going in a large coil, it likes to keep going, according to Lenz's Law. This makes it hard for the amplifier to make the speaker produce good sounds. A speaker with too large a coil would literally be fighting the amplifier. Such fighting produces poor quality sound.

Lenz's Law states that the current in a coil likes to continue flowing in the same direction. When the amplifier tries to change the current's direction, the coil itself opposes this change. The result is that the coil doesn't behave exactly the way the amplifier wants it to behave. This means that small coils are better because they resist changes in current less.

30

Soundproofing

Sometimes sound seems to travel easily between two places, and sometimes it doesn't. Some rooms seem noisy and it is hard to hear conversations when more than a few people are in the room. Other rooms seem quiet even with many people present. Why are some rooms quieter than others? What makes sound travel easily or not at all?

Sound is a wave that travels in air or in other materials. In air, the source of a sound causes a compression of the air molecules. These compressed air molecules expand into the next bunch of air molecules and compress them. This bunch then expands into the next bunch, etc. The source of sound provides energy to compress the air. The energy is exchanged between the bunches of air molecules as the sound travels. When the wave hits your ear, the energy is given to your eardrum and you hear the sound.

Sound normally travels in all directions from the source. As the sound travels, it expands into a larger and larger area. The energy is spread more and more thinly over this area. Therefore, as you get farther from a source of sound, less energy hits your ear and the sound is softer.

Rooms may be louder or quieter depending on what the walls are made of. If the walls of a room reflect the sound energy efficiently, even a large room can be noisy, even with a small source of sound. If the room is large enough, we hear echoes. Echoes are caused when sound waves hit a solid surface and the air molecules bounce back and forth without losing energy. Soft surfaces are often used to prevent echoes. When the sound waves hits a soft surface, they push on the surface and the surface moves slightly. Because it absorbs the energy of the wave, reflected sound is much softer.

Architects take advantage of the fact that soft surfaces absorb sound waves. They decorate with banners or put other pieces of cloth on the walls. People also absorb sound waves. You must amplify music more when an auditorium is filled with people than when it is empty.

Figure 30

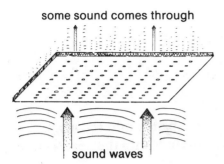

some sound comes through

sound waves

Another way to reduce sound is to have the sound waves literally go into holes and "get lost," as shown in Figure 30. Ceiling tiles in many buildings are designed this way. Above the tiles is empty space. When the sound goes through the holes, it enters this empty space and is gone from the room. The ceiling literally traps sound waves.

A final way to reduce noise is to put up barriers between the source of sound and the people in the room. These barriers are often made with soft materials that absorb sound waves and reduce levels of sound coming through.

Using these three different methods for reducing sound, it is possible to make a place quieter. If you want to prevent sound from coming into the room from outside, you make walls with sound-absorbing materials. If you want to reduce sound in the room, you need to either absorb the sound waves or trap them.

Often, when you walk into a new home, it has a strange sound to it. The reason is that the furnishings of a room absorb sound. The room becomes quieter. This is one reason why it is harder to sell a house with no furniture in it. People who look at it don't like the sound of it.

When you go into a room, think about how sound travels in it. Then think about what is in the room to absorb the sound or to reflect it back to your ears. Can you find a relationsihp between how noisy a room is and what it is like on the inside?

Review Questions

1) How does a sound wave travel and how does it transfer energy?

2) Why is there a difference in the way sound reflects off hard and soft materials?

3) What do holes in ceiling tiles do to make a room quieter?

4) Look around the room. What things do you see that absorb sound and what things reflect it?

TEACHER

Answers

1) Sound waves travel as a section of compressed air expands into the next section. That section becomes compressed, so it expands into the next section.

2) Hard surfaces reflect sound waves easily because the air molecules literally bounce off the wall with no loss of energy. Soft surfaces absorb some of the energy of the molecules so the wave becomes smaller.

3) The holes literally allow the sound to escape and leave the room.

4) Student answers will vary.

Whether a room is noisy or quiet has to do with the materials used in its construction. The formal name for the study of how sound behaves is *acoustics*. It is actually a very difficult topic to work with on a numerical level because there are so many variables. This section works with the absolute basics of how sounds travel.

Sound is a *longitudinal wave*, meaning that it travels in the direction in which the molecules move. The air molecules expand into the next group of molecules and then move back to their original positions. (Transverse waves are like waves in water where the medium goes up and down as the wave moves across the surface of the lake.) Sound waves can travel in many media, but they travel best in elastic media. An elastic medium is one that springs back to its original position after the wave travels through without losing energy. Steel is an elastic medium and carries sound easily. Cotton is not a good medium for sound to travel in because it absorbs energy.

A room can become quite noisy when filled with people. What happens is that when there are enough people in the room, sound starts reflecting back to the people who are talking. In order to be heard, they raise their voices. This, of course, means more sound reflects back, so people continue to raise their voices and it becomes difficult to hear. Some rooms—such as school lunchrooms—always seem noisy unless some effort has been made to absorb sound. Most restaurants take great pains to absorb sound energy and give patrons a pleasant dining experience.

One interesting way to reduce sound in buildings is to build them in non-rectangular shapes. The sound waves don't echo back and forth across the room, so the room sounds quieter.

31

How You See

The gift of sight lets you see the world around you. But how does your brain actually see? How does the light from a tree change into something that your brain identifies and allows you to say, "I see a tree"? What happens to change the light into the mental image?

Light from a tree comes to you as little wave packets. These packets are called *photons*. The photons travel at the speed of light from the tree to you. The speed of light is 300 million meters per second (186,000 miles/sec), so the photons get from the tree to you **very** quickly. Photons come off every point on the tree and travel in straight lines.

When the light reaches your eye, it goes through a *lens*. The lens is like a magnifying glass in that it is thicker in the middle than at the edges. The image is made on the back of your eye, which is called the *retina*, in the same way a magnifying glass can make an image, as shown in Figure 31a. If you need glasses, the lens in one or both of your eyes doesn't make a clear image on the retina. The glasses help make a clear image.

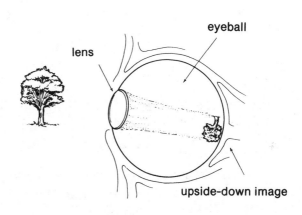

Figure 31a

The lens makes the rays of light that left a given point on the tree come back together again. For every point on the tree, there is a corresponding point for the image on your retina. The rays are brought to this point, or focus, because the light bends as it goes through the lens.

The retina is covered with cells called *rods* and *cones*. The rods work in dim light but do not see color. The cones need brighter light but they see color. We don't see color in the dark because the cones need more light. We just see black and white.

When light hits the rods and cones, the energy of the photons is changed into nerve impulses. The energy causes a chemical change in the rods and cones in what is called a *photochemical* reaction. These chemical reactions cause nerves to fire. Whether a particular nerve fires depends on the kind and amount of light that strikes it. Photochemical reactions also occur when photographic film is exposed to light. The chemical changes allow a picture to form when the film is developed.

Sometimes when you stare at something for a long time and then look away, you see what is called a *latent image*. This latent image, or after-image, occurs because the rods and cones get tired of producing the same chemicals. For short periods of time afterward, they cannot make them. You see colors because if you were looking at something red, there are less "red chemicals" present. Therefore, the color you see is the opposite of the color you looked at. It's called the "complementary color."

The nerve impulses from the rods and cones are sent to the brain through a bundle of nerves called the *optic nerve*. Where the optic nerve leaves the eye,

Figure 31b  there are no rods or cones. You don't see anything at this spot. It is called your *blind spot*. You can locate this blind spot if you use Figure 31b. Look at the **X** and **O** from a normal reading distance. Cover your left eye and look directly at the X. Now, move your head closer and then farther away until you notice that the O is not present. You must look straight at the X. You can find the blind spot for your left eye by looking at the O and covering your right eye.

When the nerve impulses get to your brain, your brain processes them into an *image*. You literally have to learn how to see. However, it happens in the first months of life so you don't remember it. At first, you see only areas of light and dark. Over a period of time, however, you begin to see better and put together a whole picture of your world. If for some reason a child is not able to see things during the first few months, he or she may never be able to see properly. The brain just can't learn how to see after it reaches a certain age.

Review Questions

1) How does light travel from an object to your eyes?

2) What function does the lens in your eye have in seeing?

3) What purpose does the retina have?

4) How is light changed into nerve impulses?

5) How do the nerve impulses get turned into an image?

TEACHER

Answers

1) Light travels in straight lines as wave packets, called photons, at the speed of light (300 million meters per second or 186,000 miles/sec).

2) The lens focuses the light to form an image on the retina.

3) The retina is where the image forms in the eye. It has the light-sensing rods and cones that change light into nerve impulses.

4) The energy of the photons is changed by a photochemical reaction to cause the nerves that send information to the brain to fire. The cones send information about color, while the rods react to less intense light and see only light and dark.

5) The nerve impulses are transferred to the brain by the optic nerve. When the impulses arrive, the brain processes the information. Vision seems to be a learned ability, and the learning is done at a very early age.

Experiments have been done where a person has worn glasses constantly to invert the image on the retina. After a period of time (and terrible headaches), the image became natural. The brain started to process the information so it was normal when upside down. (When the experimenter took off the glasses, the image became normal again after another period of time.) Remember, the image on the retina is inverted from the real world. This is a property of the images formed by lenses. It may help to demonstrate the inverted image to the students by using a magnifying glass. Hold it near a wall opposite a window. The image may not be very clear but it will show that the sky is down and the ground is up.

The lens focuses light on the retina. Muscles in the eye change its shape to allow the eye to focus at different distances. These muscles make the lens either thicker or thinner at the center.

The photochemical reaction in the rods and cones occurs with chemicals that are constantly regenerated. The nerves send information to the brain and the brain updates its picture about 20 times per second. The reactions occur because light breaks chemical bonds, this action changes the chemicals. A latent image occurs because the chemical process is tired. It lasts up to a minute or so. You can make a latent image of a red, white, and blue flag from a flag made from different colors. You may want to have some color pictures around so students can observe how colors are changed in the latent image.

The processing of nerve impulses into a mental image is still not completely understood. It is complex but automatic.

32
Printing Color Pictures in a Magazine

Did you ever wonder how colors are printed in a magazine or newspaper? As you paint a picture, you need to be careful when mixing the different colors. So how is it done on the printed page?

Printing presses use tiny color dots to give the colors you see. The dots are so small that you must use a magnifying glass to see the individual ones. Since they are so small, your eye can't see each dot, so it mixes the colors from a number of dots. The shade, or how dark the color is, is determined by the size of the dots and how many of them are used in a given area. The quality of the printing is also a factor in how small or large the color dots are. Poor quality printing generally uses larger dots.

Use a magnifying glass to study different types of color pictures. Use color newspapers, magazines, and any other color pictures available. What different patterns of dots do you see? How are the different colors made?

Start by looking at a number of different color pictures from different sources. After you have looked at a number of them to see their differences, start looking carefully at one picture. Examine the picture closely to find

1) how different shades of the same color are made

2) how different colors are made

3) how dot size seems to relate to picture quality.

Record your observations for each picture and then, as a group, see if you can make some statements about how different colors are made. Use the observations you have recorded as you were looking at your pictures. Be as specific as you can.

TEACHER

Materials Needed
magnifying glasses a wide assortment of color pictures

This exercise is interesting for students because it gives them a new way of looking at things they see every day. Color dots are also visible on a TV screen, so students can look for them there as well.

In order to run a good experiment, you must get a variety of different kinds of pictures. You should find high-quality and poor-quality pictures. You may also be able to find some pictures that don't appear to have any dots in them. These tend to be the finest quality. The dots in this case may be so small that they can't be seen even with a magnifying glass, or they may be done by a different printing process which blends the colors.

Color photographs are generally high quality, but it is possible to see what is known as *film grain*. Light enters the camera and causes small grains of light-sensitive chemicals to change so that when they are developed, a color is left on the film or paper. The smaller the film grain, the clearer the picture. However, with small film grains, most film takes longer to expose. These films are generally not suitable in poor light conditions. You may be able to find film grain in some photographs but not in others. Generally, you can find film grain in enlargements of pictures.

In this exercise, students should be encouraged to describe the things they see as carefully as they can. Initially, they will probably not be able to put into words what they see and may need to be encouraged to be complete in their descriptions. Giving the students many different examples of pictures helps them to see differences and to get started on their classifications.

33
How Colored Light Mixes

Most people are familiar with how paints mix. Red and yellow make orange, while blue and yellow make green. These colors are made by *subtractive coloring*. When you shine light of different colors onto white paper, the light adds in what is called *additive coloring*.

You probably know that you see red when red light strikes your eyes. You see yellow when yellow light strikes your eyes. Red paint absorbs all colors except red, which it reflects. Likewise, yellow paint absorbs all colors but yellow. Paints reflect the color you see and absorb the others. This is why black objects get hotter than white ones in the sun: black absorbs all light.

When you mix red and yellow paint, the combination reflects some red and some yellow, which you see as orange. If you mix red, yellow, and blue paint, you get brown because the paint absorbs some of all colors of light.

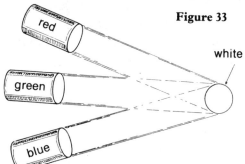

Figure 33

When you mix light of different colors, things are different. White light from the sun or from a light can be split into many colors by a prism or raindrops to form a rainbow. What happens if all these colors are put back together again? As you might have guessed, they form white light, as shown in Figure 33.

Conduct an experiment to see what happens when different colors of light shine on white paper. As you run your experiment, vary the intensity of the lights that you use. You can do this by changing the distance between your light sources and the white paper. You can also change the brightness by covering part of the light sources with your hand.

Shine the lights on a piece of white paper. See what happens when you mix red and green, red and blue, and blue and green. Then see if you can make white by using all of the lights. Vary the intensity of each light source and see what happens to the color reflected from the white page.

As you run your experiments, record what colors you are using, how you are varying the intensity of the light, and what color you see as a result. Then, make some statements about what you have learned about the mixing of colored light.

How Everyday Things Work

TEACHER

Materials Needed

flashlights
primary-color filters (cellophane or gels)

This is an experiment that allows students to see how light mixes as compared to how pigments mix. The difference is often quite startling for students. It can really excite them about science.

You need light sources for the students. Inexpensive flashlights are very good sources of light. Then you need to get filters in the three primary colors: red, green, and blue. These filters should be taped over the fronts of the flashlights so that each group has one flashlight of each color.

These filters are available from a number of different sources. You may have colored cellophane available from art projects. Another source is theater groups that use different colored "gels" in their lighting departments. A third source is a roll of color slide film. Take pictures of red, green, and blue objects. When the film is developed, the slides can be taped over the fronts of the flashlights.

Students will have some difficulty with this lab because the results might seem strange to them. It should be done in a darkened room. They must be encouraged to change the intensity of the light to see what happens when the color intensity is changed. They must also be reminded to record their observations so that they can remember what they learned from their experiments.

This lab can also be done as an entire class exercise if enough light sources are not available. In this case, the exercise can be directed more easily and it will take much less time to do.

34

How Lenses Form Images

We see our world through the lenses in our eyes. Without them, we would see only light and dark. But how do lenses work and how do they form their images?

Many lenses, like those in the eye, are *convex lenses.* They are thicker in the middle than at the edges, like a magnifying glass. Experiment with a magnifying glass or another convex lens. Hold it next to a light-colored wall opposite a window. Slowly move the lens away from the wall. Observe the light that comes through the lens and strikes the wall, as shown in Figure 34a. It makes an image, or picture, of what is outside the window. What does the image look like? If the lens in your eye is like the magnifying glass, what must the image be like on the retina, or the back of your eye? Is the image larger or smaller than the objects outside the window? What does the image that falls on your retina probably look like?

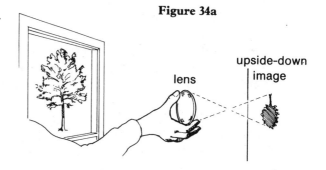

Figure 34a

lens

upside-down image

When you get a clear image of the things outside the window, use a meterstick to measure the distance the lens is from the wall. Record this value. This distance is called the *focal length* of the lens. How must the focal length of the lens in your eye compare to the focal length you just measured?

Now, take your lens and hold it near a piece of paper with printing on it. Look through the lens at the paper and slowly move it away from the paper. Move it far enough away from the paper so that it is twice the distance you measured for the focal length. What do you observe? Is there a distance from the printing where you can't see an image? Measure this distance with a meterstick. How

How Everyday Things Work

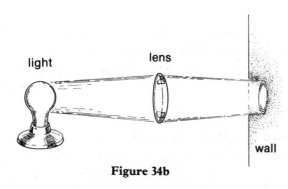

Figure 34b

does it compare to the focal length you measured earlier? What happens when you move the lens farther than the distance where you can't see an image?

Hold your lens near a small light bulb so it is between the bulb and a light-colored wall, as shown in Figure 34b. What happens as you move it away from the light bulb? Is this like a flashlight beam or a lighthouse? Do you get an image on the wall? Record your observations.

TEACHER

Materials Needed

---

convex lenses (magnifying glasses)

a light-colored wall   a bare light bulb (lamp)

This section is an introduction to how lenses work. The students investigate the focal length of a lens and see what happens when images are formed. The first part of the experiment takes advantage of a bright object that is a long distance away. This allows students to see an inverted and smaller image on the wall. (It may help if the lights in the room are turned off.) Students also see how to "focus" an image and make it as sharp as possible. Have students measure the distance from the wall to the lens when they have the sharpest image possible. This distance very closely approximates the focal length.

The second part of the experiment, which looks at an enlarged image made by a magnifyiing glass, may be something the students have already done on their own. When the lens is next to the print, the image is only slightly enlarged and upright. As the lens is moved farther away, it becomes larger until you approach the focal length. Theoretically, the image would be infinitely large when the lens is at one focal length from the print. However, no lens is perfect, and we can't see something infinitely big, so the image gets blurred and can't be seen. Then, as you move farther away, the image is inverted and becomes smaller and less and less blurred. Students should measure the distance at which the image is most blurred. This distance should equal the focal length.

The last part of the experiment examines how light can be made into a beam using a convex lens. You need a rather dark room for this to be effective. This is done in movie and slide projectors as well as theater lights and many other devices. When the lens is at its focal length, the rays of light coming from the light source become parallel and form a beam. (These beams are often made by using reflectors behind the light source, as in a flashlight, but the effect is the same. The rays become parallel.) As the lens is moved closer to the wall, students will see an image of the light bulb just before the lens is one focal length from the wall.

If you want a little more background on this topic, you can consult high school physics texts that generally have lots of diagrams showing how images are formed.

The lenses used in this experiment can be simple, and even regular magnifying glasses work. A light-colored wall is very helpful, but white pieces of paper fastened to the wall will also work well. The last section requires a bare light bulb about two meters from a wall. A regular lamp will suffice.

35

Lasers

Lasers are wonderful examples of how scientific principles can be applied to make something very useful. Lasers produce an intense form of light from solids, liquids, or gases. The light is intense because the waves of light are all doing the same thing. All the *wave crests* are together and all the *wave troughs* are together, as shown in Figure 35a.

Figure 35a

waves all doing the same thing

Lasers produce light in a special way. The verb, to lase, comes from the way light is created: **L**ight **A**mplification by **S**timulated **E**mission.

Light is hard to describe when you study it closely. Sometimes it behaves like a wave and sometimes it behaves like a particle. For this reason, scientists call light a particle wave or a *photon*.

Light is given off when electrons move closer to the nucleus, or center, of an atom. The electrons move around the atom in what are called *orbitals*. The orbitals are at specific distances from the nucleus of the atom, and each one has a different energy level. When electrons move from one orbital to another, a certain fixed amount of energy is given off as a photon. Light coming from a laser is all one wavelength, so the light is a very pure color.

A common kind of laser is a helium neon laser. It is used in checkout lines at many stores. This laser gives off a red light and is low-powered so that it can't hurt anyone. The laser has a tube surrounded by an energy source. The tube contains helium and neon atoms, and energy is provided by electricity. Electrons in the helium and neon atoms are given energy and they move away from the nucleus of the atom, or to a higher orbital. Almost immediately, they move closer to the nucleus of the atom, but many of the electrons stop before they get to their old place. They remain at a higher-than-normal orbital, as shown in Figure 35b.

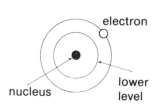

electron

nucleus

lower level

Figure 35b

How Everyday Things Work

The electrons that haven't fallen back to their normal orbital will fall if given a small push. A photon of the same energy as the atom wants to give up

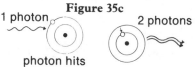

Figure 35c

can give that push. When a photon hits, the electron moves to the lower energy level and gives off its photon of light. One photon stimulates another photon to be given off, as shown in Figure 35c. The photon moves in the same direction as the first photon and vibrates the same way. Both photons have their crests together and their troughs together. These two waves act as if they were one wave with twice as much energy.

Now two photons, or light waves, are traveling together. Because many other atoms have electrons ready to give up energy, the two photons hit another atom, which adds a third photon to the group. The group hits other atoms, adding a photon each time. The original photon of light has been greatly amplified.

At each end of the laser tube, there is a mirror. One mirror reflects all the light; the other reflects perhaps 90% of the light, as shown in Figure 35d. The rest of the light, 10%, escapes from the laser as the beams we see. Ninety percent of the light

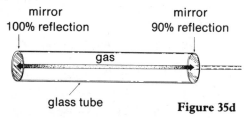

Figure 35d

bounces back down the tube, hitting more atoms on the way and picking up more photons. The result is a very intense beam of light.

All lasers work in about the same way. They use different materials, but each makes lots of photons traveling in the same direction with their crests and troughs all together. Very small lasers are used in fiber optics telephone lines. Thousands of them would be needed to give the light of one light bulb. Other lasers have enough energy to cut through metals or heat things to temperatures of millions of degrees.

Review Questions

1) What do each of the letters L A S E mean in relation to a laser?

2) How does an atom give off light?

3) Why can one photon cause another photon to be given off from an atom?

4) What happens when two photons are added together in a laser?

5) How does the beam of light become amplified in a laser and finally escape?

 How Everyday Things Work

TEACHER

Answers

1) **L**ight **A**mplification by **S**timulated **E**mission.

2) A photon of light is given off as an electron moves toward the nucleus of an atom, moving from a higher orbital to a lower one.

3) Photons are given off by stimulated emission. If the energy of the photon that hits it equals the energy of the photon that is given off, the electron changes its orbital. This is almost the reverse of the way atoms absorb the energy of photons. When atoms absorb photons, they absorb only photons containing the right amount of energy to move an electron from one orbital up to another. For example, if white light shines through a gas, dark lines can be seen in various places because the gas absorbs the photons of those energies. Photons of energies that do not correspond to proper energy level changes do not get absorbed.

4) When one photon stimulates an atom to give up a photon by stimulated emission, the second photon is given off in phase with the first photon. It goes in the same direction and with its crests and troughs in the same places as the first. This makes crests and troughs of twice the amplitude—meaning that the light is more intense or bright.

5) The beam of light starts as photons that run into each other and cause stimulated emission. Some start moving up and down the tube, so they reflect off the mirrors at each end of the tube. The mirror at one end is not completely reflective (partially silvered) so some light escapes from it in a beam.

Lasers are fascinating to students because they are the subject of many science fiction movies and futuristic weapons. Some lasers are as powerful as they are imagined to be, but many lasers are much less powerful. They are often used in medicine because they can cut tissue by burning it, which cauterizes the wound and prevents bleeding. They are also often used in eye surgery.

Lasers can be made of many different substances. They can be made of transparent crystals, from liquids, or from gases. One type of liquid laser using dyes can be tuned to the desired wavelength. This allows photons of virtually any energy to be produced if an application demands it. Some lasers are used for cutting materials or for etching computer chips to make pathways for circuits. A "Star Wars" laser was built that lased with X-rays, which have much more energy than visible light. The problem with this laser is that it requires an atomic bomb to fire it, destroying the laser in the process of firing.

36

Insulation and Heat Loss

We often try to keep things hot or cold and we use insulation to do it. Insulation prevents heat from moving from a hot place to a colder place. In winter, insulation prevents heat from leaving a warm house, while in summer it prevents heat from entering the house. In both cases, insulation slows the transfer of heat.

Figure 36a

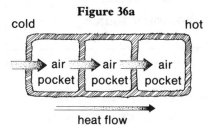

cold   hot

heat flow

Many insulators use air pockets to slow the transfer of heat. Heat going through the insulation must heat up the first air pocket, which then must heat up the next air pocket, as shown in Figure 36a. Because heat must be transferred from one pocket to another, heat moves slowly.

Some examples of insulators that have air pockets are down jackets, feathers on birds, fiberglass insulation used in houses, and pot holders. How do you know each of these contains air? Press on the down jacket and what happens? Why do birds fluff up their feathers in the cold? What happens when you press on fiberglass insulation? What is a pot holder made of?

You probably have experienced what happens if your insulation gets wet. You get cold quicker. Some insulators almost stop functioning when they get wet. Wet clothing holds almost no air pockets. A wet down jacket is useless. Seabirds caught in oil spills often die because they can't fluff their feathers. The oil takes the natural oils out of the bird's feathers and the feathers no longer stay fluffy. A bird without insulation loses heat too fast and dies.

Figure 36b

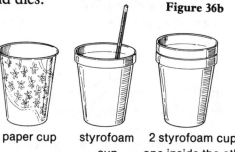

paper cup   styrofoam cup   2 styrofoam cups one inside the other

See how different kinds of insulation hold heat. Experiment with a paper cup, a styrofoam cup, and two styrofoam cups, one inside the other, as shown in Figure 36b. Put the same amount of hot water from a faucet into each cup. Measure the initial temperature. Wait 5 minutes and find the new water temperature in each cup. Then, measure the temperature every 5 minutes until the end of class. Record the time and temperature of each container of water. Which is best at keeping the water warm? Do the results agree with what you expected?

TEACHER

Materials Needed

paper cups   thermometer

styrofoam cups   hot water source

Insulation prevents heat loss; the particular qualities of the insulation determine how much heat flows through it per unit time. Thicker insulators and better quality insulators reduce heat loss. Most students know that thicker insulation is better for keeping warm, and that's why they use heavier clothing in cold weather. Some may realize that people or animals with more fat stay warmer in cold water or air. However, most students have not really thought that thicker insulation prevents heat from entering a house in warm weather. They normally think of insulation as preventing heat loss, not heat gain. Insulation prevents the flow of heat whether it is into or out of a house.

The quality of insulation is very important for the prevention of heat flow. Different kinds of building materials are rated for how they allow heat to flow through them. Glass, metal, and stone are poor insulators. This is why these substances feel cold when you touch them. Skin loses heat quickly and thus feels cool. Better insulators, like rugs or wood, don't feel cool because they prevent heat from flowing.

The ability of insulation to prevent heat from flowing may be changed under some circumstances. Wet down or wet fiberglass loses much of its insulation properties. Styrofoam insulation is not rapidly affected by water because water is prevented from entering the insulation.

The experiment suggested in this section is quite easy to run if thermometers are available. The results should show that water in the paper cup cools fastest and water in the double styrofoam cup the slowest. Also, the water temperature changes rapidly at first but changes more and more slowly as it approaches room temperature. This is because heat loss is related to the temperature difference between the hot object and the cold object. With twice the temperature difference, twice as much heat is lost in a given amount of time. As time goes by, the temperature difference between the water and the air becomes less, so the heat loss is less.

When you run the experiment, you must make sure that students record the time and the temperature correctly. They must let the thermometer stay in the water for 10 to 15 seconds to get the correct temperature. Care must be taken to have the same amount of water in each cup.

Use hot tap water so the water will not be too hot and burn the students. Also, at a higher temperature, evaporation takes away a large amount of heat in addition to the heat lost through the walls of the cup.

37

Ice Skates

Moving rapidly over a frozen lake or across an ice rink is wonderful to experience. But what allows the skates to travel so easily? Why don't they slide on other surfaces? What makes ice so special?

Figure 37a

ice   liquid water

Ice is different from most substances because when it freezes it expands rather than contracts. Ice expands when it freezes because the molecules form crystals that literally have hollow cores. The crystals take up more room than water in the liquid state. Because the crystals take more room, the ice expands, as shown in Figure 37a.

When you ice skate, you put a great pressure on the ice. Pressure is force exerted per unit area. Gravity pulls down on you and you exert a force on the ice. You sharpen your ice skates to make the area touching the ice as small as possible. With a small area, the gravitational force exerts a large pressure on the ice.

The large pressure pushes on the ice crystals making them change into a form in which they are closer together. Because the water molecules are closer together in the liquid form, pressure makes the molecules under your skates turn into liquid water. The water makes a nearly frictionless surface between the ice and the skate and you can easily slide. After your skate moves past, the water quickly refreezes behind it.

You can run an experiment to see how ice melts with pressure. Take a piece of ice which has been made in a quart milk carton in a freezer. Use two supports separated by about 10 cm (3 in) to hold your ice block, as shown in Figure 37b. Make sure that you protect the supports and floor from water damage.

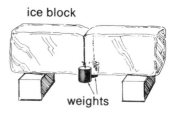

ice block

weights

Figure 37b

Take a piece of thin wire and make two loops, one in each end. Then attach equal weights to each loop. Place the wire over the ice so the weights hang on opposite sides of the ice. Observe what happens and record your observations. You may have to wait a few minutes to see a difference. Experiment with a variety of weights and see what happens. What causes the things that you observe?

How Everyday Things Work

$$\boxed{\textbf{Teacher}}$$

Materials Needed	
weights	supports
wire	block of ice

Most students have either skated or seen ice skaters glide across ice. Many don't know why it is possible. We know it is not possible to skate on iron or wax or plastic. These substances don't have the strange property that ice has, namely, that it expands upon freezing.

You may want to draw attention to this expansion upon freezing by showing the students a few things. The ice blocks you make for the experiment show expansion upon freezing. You can also draw a line on a frozen ice cube tray and then see what happens when the ice melts.

Water expands almost 10% upon freezing. The density of ice is therefore about 90% of water. This causes ice cubes and icebergs to float in water. It also causes ice to form on the top of a lake and not sink. If ice sank it probably would not melt during the summer months. It would remain and make it impossible for bottom-dwelling organisms to live.

This activity shows how pressure can cause ice to melt. The weights exert a force on the wire. Because the wire is thin, a large pressure is exerted on the ice, melting the ice under the wire. The liquid water then moves above the wire and refreezes because it is no longer under pressure. The process repeats as the wire moves through the ice. Larger weights or thinner wire make the wire sink through the ice faster because of greater pressure.

If the pressure is not great enough to cause melting, the wire moves very slowly—if at all. This is similar to what happens when you try to skate on dull ice skates. The dull skates' surface area is too large. Therefore, the pressure is not great enough to melt the ice and the skates don't work well. You might have the students investigate this effect by having different groups put different weights on the wires.

How a Thermostat Works

A thermostat is used to turn things on or off when the temperature reaches a certain value. A thermostat turns on a heater when the temperature drops too low or turns on a refrigerator when the temperature rises too high. But how does the thermostat know when to turn something on or off and how does it do it?

Actually, there are two kinds of thermostats. The first one has been used for a long time and works well for many machines. The second one, called a *thermistor,* is similar to a transistor in the way it works and has only been around for a few decades.

The first kind of thermostat used in most houses is made of two thin metal strips stuck together. The strips are made out of different kinds of metal and behave differently when they heat up or cool down. This combination of two metal strips stuck together is called a "bimetallic" strip. ("Bi" means two.)

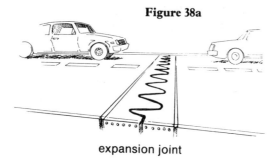

Figure 38a

expansion joint

When metals are heated, they expand. A metal strip becomes larger when heated. The amount that it expands is not large, however. A 100-meter (300 ft) piece of iron will expand about .2 meters (8 in) as it is heated from 0°C to 25°C (32°F to 100°F). This expansion of metals must be taken into account when you build things from steel. Bridge designers must put in movable expansion joints (as shown in Figure 38a) or the bridge might fall down.

A thermostat is made of two kinds of metal. Each kind expands a different amount when it changes one degree of temperature. This difference in expansion causes the bimetallic strip to change shape. If the length of each of the metal strips is initially the same, the bimetallic strip is straight. If one becomes longer than the other then the bimetallic strip bends into an arc. The longer strip is on the outside of the curve and the smaller one is on the inside.

In a thermostat, a bimetallic strip is held in place at one end and the other end is near a small switch. When the temperature changes and the strip bends to a different shape, the strip pushes on an electrical switch, as shown in Figure 38b.

Figure 38b

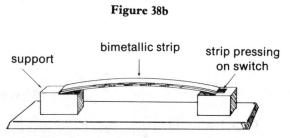

support bimetallic strip strip pressing on switch

Thermostats often don't turn on a heater directly. They may use a *relay* instead. Because there is danger if you touch high voltages, a thermostat often uses low voltage. This low voltage causes another switch or relay to turn on the needed equipment.

A thermistor works in a different way from a bimetallic strip. It is a device similar to a transistor, but it increases its electrical resistance as the temperature drops. A large electrical resistance makes it hard for current to flow. A small resistance makes it easier for current to flow. A thermostat using a thermistor turns a device on or off when the resistance of the thermistor reaches a certain point.

Thermistors are used for many purposes other than turning heaters on and off. They can be used to tell temperature in electric thermometers, car engines, or outside of a jet plane. Thermistors are very useful because they tell the temperature for a range of values. A thermostat just turns on or off at a particular value. The thermistor can be attached to a computer to measure the thermistor's resistance. The computer then makes appropriate decisions about what to do at that particular temperature. Thermistors are used by computers in modern cars. Because gasoline must be put into an engine in different amounts as the engine warms up, the computer and thermistors allow the engine to make appropriate adjustments that improve performance and fuel economy and reduce pollution.

Review Questions

1) What is a bimetallic strip and why does it bend with a change in temperature?

2) How is a thermostat constructed with a bimetallic strip?

3) How is a thermistor different from a regular thermostat?

4) What is the advantage of a thermistor over a bimetallic strip?

TEACHER

Answers

1) A bimetallic strip is made of two different types of metal fastened together. Because the metals expand at different rates, the strip bends in different amounts as the temperature changes.

2) A thermostat uses a bimetallic strip to press a switch at a particular temperature.

3) A thermistor is similar to a transistor, but it increases resistance as the temperature drops and decreases resistance when the temperature rises. (This is the opposite of what happens when normal conductors change temperature.) Also, thermistors can be built so that large changes in resistance occur with small changes in temperature.

4) The thermistor can be used to tell the temperature, not just to turn something on and off.

Students are familiar with thermostats, although they probably don't know how they work. Most likely, students will not know about thermistors, but they should find them interesting to study.

Regular bimetallic strip thermostats have been around for a long time. They take advantage of very small changes in the amount that solids expand or contract with a change in temperature. Solids expand when heated and contract when cooled. Typically, they expand by $1/100,000$ (10^{-5}) of their length when they change $1°C$. This small change is not noticeable in most situations, but it can easily be seen in large bridges. It is also the reason that concrete blocks are used for sidewalks instead of one continuous section. The cracks between the blocks allow the blocks to expand when they are heated.

The difference in the expansion of the two metals in the bimetallic strip causes the strip to bend. The longer strip makes a circle of a larger radius, while the other piece of metal makes a circle of a smaller radius. If both strips are the same length, then no bending occurs.

The bending of the metal causes a small switch, called a microswitch, to turn current on or off. Generally, a small difference in temperature exists between when the thermostat turns on and off. In a heater, the bimetallic strip must warm up a few degrees above the temperature it turns on to make the heater turn off. Otherwise, the device would turn on and off too often.

Thermistors are more flexible than thermostats because they can tell a range of temperatures rather than just the temperature to turn something on or off. They need a small computer (generally quite inexpensive—less than $100) to analyze the information. In cars, however, thermistors are useful because the computer can give different instructions to the engine as the temperature rises. Electric thermometers can give continuous readouts of temperatures and this, too, has its advantages.

Thermistors work the opposite of resistors in that they decrease their resistance with an increase in temperature. They can also be built to produce a large change in resistance in response to a small change in temperature.

39

How Dew Forms

Dew often forms on the ground in the morning after a clear, still night. But where does this water come from? Why does it form on some nights and not on others?

Figure 39a

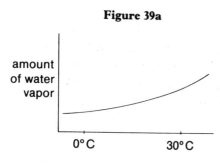

Dew forms because the air cools. When air cools, it cannot hold as much water in the vapor, or gas, phase, as shown in Figure 39a. The extra water *condenses* or is turned back into a liquid. Generally, when water changes from the gas to the liquid phase, it needs a place to condense. With dew, grass blades are prime spots.

But why does dew form on some nights and not on others? The temperature at which dew starts forming is called the *dew point*. On some nights it does not cool enough to reach the dew point. On a clear night, heat from the ground easily radiates, or travels, into the sky. This cools the ground rapidly because large amounts of heat leave. On nights with cloud cover, heat is reflected by the clouds back to earth. The ground doesn't cool as much. Dew tends to form on clear nights, not on cloudy ones.

Of course, it is harder for dew to form if there is less water vapor or moisture in the air. In deserts, less dew forms than in moist places. Even in deserts, though, some dew forms, and some animals literally drink all their water for the day from the morning dew.

When the temperature is below freezing, frost forms on the ground for the same reason that dew forms. The water vapor freezes instead of remaining as water.

You can run some experiments to see how dew forms. You need a glass, water, ice, and a thermometer. Fill the glass half full with water and measure the temperature of the water. Add small pieces of ice to the water. Keep stirring the water and measure the temperature when you first start seeing water condense on the outside of the glass, as shown in Figure 39b. "Dew" is forming on your glass. Try running your experiment on another day with a different amount of humidity in the air. What results do you notice?

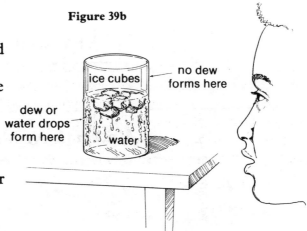

Figure 39b

no dew forms here

ice cubes

dew or water drops form here

water

TEACHER

Materials Needed	
a glass	ice
water	thermometer

This experiment is easy to do and students can see when condensation occurs. The temperature at which the condensation starts is called the *dew point*. It is determined by the amount of water in the air. More water in the air means a higher dew point. The relative humidity is a measure of how much water is in the air. Water will start condensing when the relative humidity is 100%.

In order to get repeatable results from the different groups, you should crush the ice beforehand. Small pieces allow the water to cool more slowly, so students can get a more accurate temperature. It may take a short time for the dew to be noticeable on the glass, so a slow cooling rate gives more accurate results. They must also look carefully at the glass to find when the first dew forms.

The dew point is an important temperature because it is hard for the temperature to fall much below it on a given night. Condensing water releases large amounts of heat so once dew starts to form, the temperature drops much more slowly than before it started to form.

Farmers' crops can be damaged by frosts, so farmers must use various methods to avoid them. If plants are covered, then the heat from the ground reflects off the cover back to the ground and saves the plant. Likewise, farmers often make artificial clouds using smoke to try to "blanket" their crops.

40

How Refrigerators and Air Conditioners Work

Refrigerators and air conditioners are wonderful devices. But how does household electricity make things cold? Obviously, if you don't plug the refrigerator in, it doesn't get cold. But why does putting electrical energy into the refrigerator make it work? Don't we use electrical energy to cook toast in a toaster? So how does something get cooled with electricity?

The refrigerator works using basic physics principles. When a gas is compressed, it heats up. The reverse is also true: when a gas expands, it cools. The refrigerator compresses a gas and then allows it to expand. The final result is that things get cold.

The electricity that goes into a refrigerator runs a compressor, a machine that compresses gas. The gas in most refrigerators is called a *fluorocarbon* (which can destroy ozone if it is released). The compressed gas becomes hot. This hot gas is not wanted in the refrigerator so it flows into tubing on the back of the refrigerator and heats the air of the room. As the gas loses heat to the room, it cools. The cooler the gas gets, the better. Spiderwebs and dust prevent the tubes from cooling efficiently, which is why the tubing on the back of the refrigerator should be kept clean.

The gas in the tubes eventually cools to nearly room temperature. It then enters the refrigerator and is allowed to expand. The gas, which was near room temperature, now cools to well below freezing. This cold gas is moved around in the walls of the refrigerator. Heat from inside the refrigerator is absorbed by the cold gas. When the gas has warmed up too much, the compressor compresses it and the process starts again. Figure 40 shows how the gas moves through a refrigerator.

When you open the door of a refrigerator, you let in warm air. This heat is removed by

Figure 40

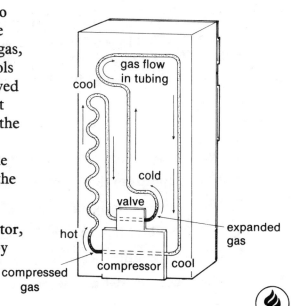

© 1992 J. Weston Walch, Publisher

How Everyday Things Work

the compressor and the flow of gas around the refrigerator. Any heat that enters is moved back out into the room. For this reason, it is not possible to cool a room using a refrigerator. Heat that goes into the refrigerator returns to the room.

An air conditioner works on the same basic principle as a refrigerator, but the coils are on the outside of the building or car. Heat is moved outdoors rather than just out of the refrigerator.

In air conditioners, as in refrigerators, heat flows from hot to cold. It flows from the hot tubes full of compressed gas to the cooler air outside. Then heat flows to the cold expanded gas in the tubes inside the house.

Frost-free refrigerators are convenient but they waste energy. Every day or so, the compressor turns off and heating coils in the walls of the freezer turn on. These heating coils melt the frost that forms in the freezer. The water then drains out and is collected in a pan. During the rest of the day the water evaporates, so it doesn't make a mess. After you heat the walls of the freezer, you have to cool them again. It is sort of funny that you put a heater in your freezer because you must then remove that heat. This is why frost-free refrigerators use more energy.

You can experience the change in temperature when a gas is compressed or allowed to expand. Place your finger over the end of a bicycle pump where the air comes out. Then push on the pump as hard as you can. The air that escapes past your finger is warm. You have compressed the air in the tube, so it is heated.

You can observe how an exanding gas cools with a bicycle tire. Pump the tire up to its full pressure and then allow the air to escape quickly through the nozzle. If you hold a thermometer right near the valve where the air is escaping, you can note the change in temperature.

Review Questions

1) What two principles allow a refrigerator to operate?

2) What happens to the gas after it leaves the compressor?

3) What causes a refrigerator to cool?

4) How does heat flow in a refrigerator?

5) What is the difference between a refrigerator and an air conditioner?

6) How does a frost-free freezer operate?

$$\boxed{\textbf{TEACHER}}$$

Materials Needed		
bicycle pump	bicycle	thermometer

Answers

1) The gas is compressed, which causes its temperature to rise. After it cools to near room temperature, the expansion of the gas causes the gas to cool.

2) The hot gas cools down to room temperature as it moves in the coils on the back of the refrigerator.

3) The gas expands and cools. The cold gas in the tubes absorbs heat from the refrigerator and cools it.

4) Heat always flows from hot objects to cooler objects.

5) The coils of a refrigerator are generally inside the house, whereas the coils for an air conditioner are outside the house. Any heat removed from the cold place must be taken somewhere. If the purpose is to cool the whole room, then you must put the heat from the coils outside of the room.

6) A frost-free freezer needs heating coils to melt the frost. The freezer must then be cooled off after the melting is finished. This wastes large amounts of energy because any added heat from the heating coils must sooner or later be removed by the compressor.

The process by which a refrigerator or an air conditioner works involves basic physics. The electrical energy runs a compressor which compresses the gas, causing its temperature to rise. After heat is transferred to the room, then the gas does work as it expands. The energy to do this work comes from the internal energy of the gas, the motion of the molecules. With less energy, the gas becomes cooler. This cold gas takes heat energy from the refrigerator to cool the food inside.

Many people think that if you open a refrigerator door the room will cool. This is true initially, but any heat that goes into the refrigerator's open door gets moved out onto the coils on the back of the refrigerator.

The two brief experiments in this section are quick to do. You may wish to demonstrate or run them in separate groups. The heating effect from compressing the air in the pump is easy to demonstrate. The cooling effect is smaller, so placing a thermometer in the escaping air stream is most likely the best way to show the result.

41

How Water Striders
Stay on Top of the Water

Water striders are little bugs with six legs that literally move on top of the water. They never get their feet wet. How do they do this? Is there some trick?

The reason they don't get their feet wet is that water has what is called *surface tension.* Surface tension causes a thin film of water to form on the surface. The water molecules hold onto each other more tightly at the surface than in the rest of the water. Water striders literally don't weigh enough to break the bonds holding the film together, so they stay on top.

But why does surface tension occur? Each molecule in the water has a certain desire to attach to other molecules. Below the surface of the water, the water molecules grab onto molecules in all directions. This spreads the total force between many molecules. Molecules at the surface don't have any molecules above them; there are only molecules below and beside them, as shown in Figure 41. The result is that surface molecules hold onto these other molecules more tightly.

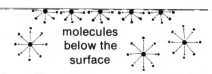

molecules at the surface

molecules below the surface

Figure 41

Because the surface molecules hold onto each other more tightly, a thin film is formed. The film pulls to make the number of molecules on the surface as small as possible. A water strider has a greasy substance on its feet that repels water. When a water strider steps on the water, it doesn't get its feet wet. The feet push down on the water but the more they push, the larger the surface of the water must be. (This is similar to what happens when you push on a balloon. The rubber doesn't want to stretch, so it pushes back on you.) The water strider makes only a small dent in the water's flat surface and doesn't sink.

Review Questions

1) How does a water strider stay on top of the water?

2) What causes surface tension?

3) What other things might be able to stay on top of the water because of surface tension? Have you seen these objects or animals?

         How Everyday Things Work

┌─────────────────┐
│ **TEACHER**   │
└─────────────────┘

Materials Needed		
balloons	wire
jar	soap
spring scale	objects to float

Answers

1) It stays there because surface tension is strong enough to prevent it from falling though.

2) The surface molecules have fewer molecules to hold onto, so they hold onto them more tightly. This makes a film that is the result of the molecules trying to make the surface as small as possible.

3) Small bugs and beetles as well as thin pieces of metal and glass can float on the surface.

Surface tension is a phenomenon of the top few molecules in a liquid. The bonding of these molecules is stronger because they have fewer molecules to bond with. The surface layer acts as a sheet that floats on the rest of the water. In a small stream it is sometimes possible to see this surface layer being blown upstream by the wind as the rest of the water is flowing downstream.

The idea that the foot of the water strider attempts to make a larger surface area out of the water may be hard for students to understand. Use a popped balloon to show the increase in force and the change in surface area. Stretch the balloon over the mouth of a wide-mouth jar or a hoop and then have the students push on the balloon. They will see that as they push on the balloon, the area increases. They will also experience a force.

Water drops form because surface tension makes the surface of a drop the smallest possible surface that will still contain the drop. A sphere has the smallest surface-area-to-volume possible.

It is possible to measure the force associated with surface tension if you have a very sensitive spring scale. You can put a thin wire loop into water and then pull it with the spring scale, being careful to pull the loop out of the water vertically. The size of the force you measure to move the wire minus the gravitational force on the wire equals the surface tension force.

Surface tension can be reduced by adding substances like soap to the water. You can sink a floating razor blade by adding a drop of soap (and waiting a bit) because the soap molecules interfere with the bonding of the surface molecules.

You may want to demonstrate surface tension for the students. It is possible to float things on the surface of water such as a double-edged razor blade (being careful not to hurt yourself). It is also possible to float needles and other things as well, if done with care. Try floating some objects that are made out of materials that normally sink. Adding soap to the water destroys the surface tension and, given a bit of time, sinks these objects.

42

Why Dogs Pant

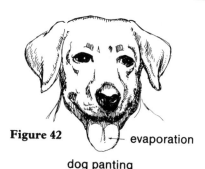

Figure 42 — evaporation

dog panting

Dogs keep cool by panting. But why does this keep them cool? Why don't they keep cool the way humans do?

Dogs pant because they do not have sweat glands. In order to take advantage of cooling by evaporation, they evaporate water from their lungs and tongues to stay cool, as shown in Figure 42. Evaporation cools because lots of energy is needed to break the bonds that hold water in the liquid form. Lots of energy must be used in order to evaporate water. The source of the energy is the dog that needs to be cooled.

Humans and many other animals sweat on the surface of their bodies. This cools the body, but it can make your clothing wet. This is OK if you can go inside and change your clothes. However, this can be a problem in cold weather. If you have to sit around in wet clothes, you get very cold. Winter hikers have to be careful about sweating into their clothes. This is why they dress in many layers, so they can take off just the right number of layers to prevent sweating. If you are winter camping, it is hard to dry wet clothing, and wet clothing doesn't insulate as well as dry clothing. Sweating into your clothing can make the difference between a comfortable trip and one where you are constantly cold.

Dogs are related to their wild cousins, wolves. Wolves live in places where it is cold in the winter. Obviously they cannot change their clothes. Therefore, when they run in the winter to catch food, they cannot take off layers of clothes to stay at the right temperature. They also can't sweat into their fur and ruin its insulating properties. Therefore, wolves sweat from their lungs and tongues, which are normally wet anyway. By panting, air is rapidly moved over these wet places and water evaporates. The dog or wolf is cooled through panting. It is in many ways similar to the way humans are cooled by sweating. The dogs don't ruin their insulation and they keep cool while exercising.

Review Questions

1) Why is evaporation a cooling process?

2) What is the problem with sweating in cold weather?

3) Why is panting better than sweating for wolves and dogs?

How Everyday Things Work

TEACHER

Answers

1) Evaporation involves breaking liquid bonds and takes large amounts of energy. In this case, the energy comes from either the panting dog or the panting wolf.

2) Sweating ruins insulation. If you can't dry the insulation, you get cold quickly once you stop exercising.

3) Panting allows evaporation from the tongue and lungs, which doesn't affect the insulation of the fur.

A panting dog looks very uncomfortable. The cooling it gets from panting is actually quite an efficient way of maintaining body temperature. The dog, like animals that sweat, is taking advantage of evaporative cooling. Evaporation takes large amounts of energy; when you sweat, you lose large amounts of energy. The amount of energy required to evaporate a gram of water is more than five times the energy required to raise one gram of water from the freezing point to the boiling point. No wonder evaporation is used to keep cool.

All animals must have a strategy for getting rid of unwanted heat. The strategy may be related to the place the animal lives. Elephants, for example, use their ears as radiators and flap them to move air across them.

Desert hares have a unique strategy for getting rid of heat. They have huge ears to radiate heat in the same way. They normally don't go underground, where many other desert animals go in the heat of the day, so they hide in the shade of a bush. They literally radiate heat to the sky. The sky to the north (in the northern hemisphere) is cooler than the surrounding desert. Infrared radiation from the ears is given off to this cooler place that doesn't return much infrared radiation to the hare. If the hare faced a hot rock, the rock would radiate more heat to the hare than the hare would radiate to the rock. The net effect would be that the hare would become hotter.

43

Why Evaporation Cools

Water cools when it evaporates. You have experienced this when you get out of the shower or after swimming. Your skin immediately starts to cool as the water changes from a liquid to a gas. Humans and many animals take advantage of this effect when they sweat. The evaporating water helps cool the body and prevents it from overheating. But why does evaporation cool?

Evaporation occurs when molecules of liquid water break the bonds that hold them together. They escape into the air. In the liquid state, water molecules are bonded with one another; in the gas phase, called *water vapor,* they are not bound in any way to one another. Energy is required to break the liquid bonds and allow the molecules to go free, as shown in Figure 43.

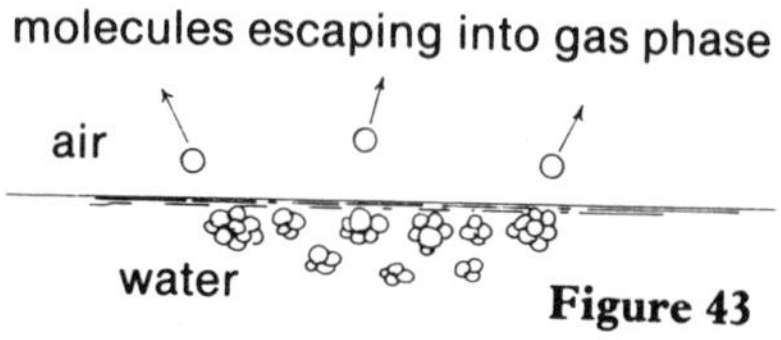

molecules escaping into gas phase

air

water

Figure 43

The energy to break the bonds comes from the random motion of molecules in the liquid water. The faster the motion, the hotter the object is because the temperature of an object is determined by the average energy that the molecules have. (Kinetic energy is related to the velocity squared.) If an object's molecules are given more energy, then the object is warmed. Take energy away and the object cools.

As the liquid molecules bump into each other, one molecule sometimes gains energy while the other molecule loses it. If the molecule gains enough energy to break the bond, it evaporates. Therefore, molecules that gain energy leave, while the less energetic molecules remain. Because temperature is related to the energy of the molecules, the remaining water cools. As you might expect, hot water evaporates faster than cool water. The molecules are moving more rapidly and need to gain less energy.

Experiment to see how temperature affects evaporation. Put equal amounts of water into two pans. Place the pan with warm water in the sun and the one with cool water in the shade. Compare how long it takes for the water to evaporate from each pan and record the average temperature of the water as it evaporates. Do your results agree with what you would expect? What happens if there is a wind? Use a fan to see if you can speed evaporation.

TEACHER

Materials Needed
sources of sun and shade
pans   water   fans

Most students are aware of evaporation as a cooling process. However, they don't really know exactly how it works or what affects the rate of evaporation. With a little more knowledge, they can understand more about why they get cool after getting out of a lake on a windy day and why sweating is a cooling process.

Evaporation takes place because of the random motion of molecules. In the liquid water, some molecules at the surface gain enough energy to break their bonds. When they break the bonds, they take energy away from the liquid water that remains. The water cools.

The amount of water in the air also affects the rate of evaporation. When the air is full of water vapor, it is hard for more water molecules to escape. Once a few molecules do evaporate, then the air is full of water vapor and can take no more. You won't feel cool unless molecules evaporate. Sweating doesn't help cool the body in humid conditions. Dry desert air is more comfortable than humid air of the same temperature because it is easier for sweat to evaporate from the skin, so cooling is more efficient. This is why you can tolerate higher temperatures in the desert. Likewise, winds make hot days more comfortable because the water that evaporates is taken away by the wind. Then more water can evaporate into air that has less water vapor.

The experiments with evaporation explore the differences in evaporation rates. The differences in temperature are easy to do. You might try placing ice under the pan to keep it at zero degrees if you have time. You should find the mass of the water before and after the evaporation because not all the water may evaporate in the time allowed. Different rates of evaporation with varying amounts of humidity in the air are more difficult to experiment with. However, you can repeat the experiment on another day with a noticeably different humidity. Changing the wind can be done with a fan. Don't use a hot plate for heating the water because it can cause burns.

Why Ice Cubes
Are Used to Cool Drinks

You often add ice to a drink to keep it cold for a long time. But how does ice keep things cold? Ice keeps drinks cold because it changes its "state" from a solid to a liquid.

The temperature of an object is related to how fast its molecules are moving. The faster they move, the higher the temperature. A cold drink, which

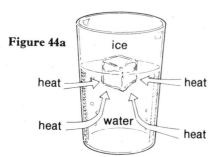

Figure 44a

is mostly water, warms up as molecules gain energy from the room. The drink's molecules move faster and when they gain too much energy, the drink is no longer cold. When ice cubes are added, things are a bit different. Lots of energy is needed to melt the ice. Therefore, when heat from the air is gained by the drink, it goes to melting the ice rather than warming the drink, as shown in Figure 44a. If the temperature rises slightly above freezing, 0°C, more ice melts and returns the drink to 0°C. Only after all the ice has melted will the drink warm up.

Lots of energy is needed to melt ice because bonds between the water molecules must be broken. The rigid bonds in solid ice make it so you can't change its shape. Liquid water has less-tightly bound molecules and it doesn't hold its shape. Breaking the bonds that hold ice in its fixed shapes takes energy. In the same way that you use energy to break a stick of wood, energy must be used to break the bonds holding the water molecules together, as shown in Figure 44b.

Figure 44b

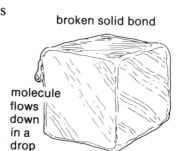

broken solid bond

molecule flows down in a drop

Run an experiment to see what happens to temperature as ice melts. Take a cup half full of hot water and measure the temperature with a thermometer. Add an ice cube to the cup and find the temperature of the water when the ice cube has melted. Now, repeat the experiment but add about the same volume of cold water as the ice you added. What is the final temperature? What causes the largest change in temperature? Does this agree with what you expected? How much cold water do you have to add to get the temperature change you got with one ice cube?

How Everyday Things Work

┌─────────────────┐
│ **TEACHER**   │
└─────────────────┘

Materials Needed

ice	cup
hot water	thermometer

This mostly qualitative experiment is designed to give the idea of how much more effective ice cubes are in cooling than cold water. Students are asked to make rough temperature measurements. The differences should be quite obvious without doing further calculations.

Hot tap water is a good starting temperature for the water. The ice cube which is added should lower the temperature significantly, but all the ice will melt. You may have to find the proper ice cube size so it melts completely. The difference should be obvious even when students add only an approximately equal amount of cold water to fresh hot water. If you have the materials available, you may want to find the mass of the ice before it is added, and then add a similar amount of water. (Remember, 1 cubic centimeter of water has a mass of 1 gram.) This may provide more convincing results.

You may want to extend the experiment by having the students actually add cold water until it cools the hot water to the temperature that the ice cube produced. If you do this, it is best if you use ice water (water at 0°C), and you will need larger cups.

The difference between ice versus water for cooling is that breaking the solid bonds requires large amounts of heat. As heat enters the cup, it goes to breaking the bonds of the ice before it warms the water. It takes 80 calories to melt one gram of ice at 0°C, whereas it takes only 100 calories to raise one gram of water from 0°C to 100°C. The large amount of heat required to melt ice means that lots of heat can enter the cup without melting the ice.

Generally, quite a bit of energy is required to have any change of state—from solid to liquid or liquid to vapor. It occurs with all materials, because bonds must be broken in order to change the state. Sometimes the energy required to change to the vapor state can be quite large. Water requires 539 calories per gram to boil water to steam.

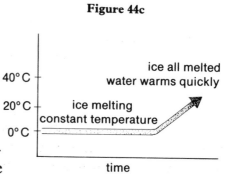

Figure 44c

You may want to do another exercise in conjunction with this one. You can plot the temperature versus time for a cup with an ice cube in it. If you use a paper cup, you will have heat enter the cup faster and the experiment is quicker. You should find that the temperature stays at 0°C until the ice is melted, and then it rises quickly. Plotting temperature versus time makes the effect of the ice very obvious. A sample graph is shown in Figure 44c.

45

How Does the Sun Shine?

The sun warms the earth and allows life to exist. It provides us with most of our energy and with light. But how does it keep giving off light? Will it ever stop shining?

The answer to the second question is that the sun has been burning for 5 billion years and should burn for another 5 billion years. It won't change very much, but how will it burn for so long? What does it use for fuel?

The fuel for the sun is hydrogen, the simplest of atoms. It is a single proton surrounded by one electron. The sun's mass is about 75% hydrogen and because the sun has a million times the mass of the earth, it has LOTS of fuel.

The sun doesn't burn its fuel in the same way hydrogen burns on earth. On earth, hydrogen and oxygen burn to form water in a **chemical** reaction. In the sun, hydrogen is burned in a **nuclear** reaction, which gives off much more energy than a chemical reaction.

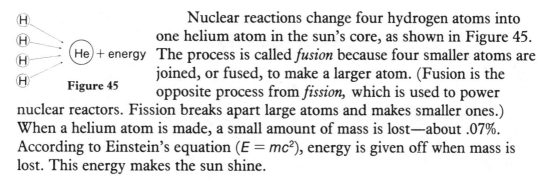

Figure 45

Nuclear reactions change four hydrogen atoms into one helium atom in the sun's core, as shown in Figure 45. The process is called *fusion* because four smaller atoms are joined, or fused, to make a larger atom. (Fusion is the opposite process from *fission,* which is used to power nuclear reactors. Fission breaks apart large atoms and makes smaller ones.) When a helium atom is made, a small amount of mass is lost—about .07%. According to Einstein's equation ($E = mc^2$), energy is given off when mass is lost. This energy makes the sun shine.

In order to have hydrogen fuse, positively charged protons must be brought together to form a larger atom. But like charges repel, so the protons repel each other. When you try to push them together, they push apart. Fusion occurs when you get the protons close enough together that another force, called the strong nuclear force, overpowers the electric force. Then the helium atom can form.

But how can the positively charged protons get close enough to fuse? Fusion occurs in the center, or the *core*, of the sun. In the core, the temperature is very hot, 10 million degrees. The pressure is also huge because the weight of the rest of the sun is pushing on it. Because atoms move faster when they are hot, they move very fast when they are at a temperature of 10 million degrees. The electric force is not strong enough to stop them. They collide and join together.

Fusion occurs only in the core of the sun. The core is at a high enough temperature and pressure for fusion to occur. The high pressure makes the hydrogen very dense, meaning that the atoms are very close together. In order for two protons to fuse, the positively charged protons must hit other protons head-on. If the gas is very dense, the chances of having a proton hit another proton head-on are much greater. Therefore, the core of the sun, with its high temperature and very dense gas, is the only place where fusion can occur.

The energy released by fusion results from the strength of the nuclear force that holds the helium nucleus together. It is very, very strong. Once it overpowers the electric force, it releases huge amounts of energy. The energy is millions of times more than is released in chemical burning. This energy source will allow the sun to burn for a total of 10 billion years. You won't have to worry about the sun burning out!

Review Questions

1) What fuel keeps the sun burning and how much of this fuel does the sun have?

2) What happens in the fusion process to produce energy?

3) Why are high temperatures and pressures needed to have fusion occur?

4) What force holds atoms together in the nucleus?

5) How old is the sun and how much longer will it burn?

┌─────────────────┐
│   **TEACHER**   │
└─────────────────┘

Answers

1) The sun burns hydrogen fuel, and about 75% of the sun is made of hydrogen. With a mass of 2×10^{30} kg, there is a lot of hydrogen.

2) Hydrogen atoms join together to form helium and some mass is lost. The lost mass has turned into energy.

3) High temperatures are needed so the protons can overcome the repulsive electric forces (positive charges repel) and finally let the nuclear force hold them together. Pressures need to be high so the density of hydrogen is great. This allows more collisions to occur.

4) The strong nuclear force holds the nucleus together and is the source of the released energy.

5) The sun is 5 billion years old and will burn for another 5 billion years.

Fusion occurs when the strong nuclear force can pull two nuclei together. In order to overcome the normal repulsive electric forces, the nuclei must have lots of kinetic energy. Kinetic theory says that they can get this kinetic energy when they are at a very high temperature.

Fusion on earth must overcome the same obstacles. Hydrogen bombs use atomic bombs with plutonium or uranium to heat and compress the atoms that are to be fused. Attempts to get controlled fusion involve either lasers to heat and compress or magnetic bottles. Neither of these methods has yet been successful in giving off more energy than has been put into the reaction.

Nuclear reactions allow the sun to give off a great deal of energy because they are much more energetic than chemical reactions. An atomic bomb can be made out of 20 pounds of plutonium and have the explosive power of more than a thousand tons of TNT. This difference between chemical and nuclear energy is hard for most people to understand. However, the sun could not produce enough energy with chemical reactions.

The energy produced in the sun's core actually takes thousands of years to be released. This is because the sun is so huge. In the inner part of the sun, the heat comes out by radiation, while in the outer part it comes out by convection. Because the sun is so dense, the transfer of heat by radiation is very slow. Photons keep hitting atoms on their way to the outside. Because the atoms are so closely packed, a photon bounces around for thousands of years before it reaches the area where convection occurs.

After another 5 billion years, the core of the sun will be filled with helium, so fusion cannot continue there. According to present theory, fusion will start to occur farther from the center in a shell just outside the core. When this happens, in order to get rid of the heat that is generated, the surface of the sun will expand to about the orbit of Venus. The surface will be red-hot and the sun will be called a Red Giant. It will take up a quarter of the sky. The temperature of earth will rise and our planet will be uninhabitable.

To continue the story, the sun will briefly fuse helium into carbon to get energy but will then turn into a White Dwarf, which will be about the size of the earth but have a density a million times that of water. Slowly it will radiate heat energy and will cool off, until it becomes a Black Dwarf in about 40 billion years.

46

Avalanches

Avalanches start when too much snow falls on steep mountain slopes. Eventually, gravity pulls the snow down the mountain. But what conditions make some snow slide and some stay on the slope?

Because avalanches are dangerous, it is important to know when they are going to occur. At ski areas and along roads in mountain passes, trained people use explosives to deliberately start avalanches. The worst avalanche is the one you don't expect.

Avalanches occur because snow comes in different forms. Snow falling from the sky can be very wet or very dry. It can have big, soft flakes or small, icy pellets. The variation occurs because snow forms at different temperatures and with different amounts of water vapor. Snow formed at warm temperatures has a larger water content than snow formed at colder ones. Also, the temperature in clouds can vary with height. Snow may form, then melt, then refreeze. As you might imagine, the crystals of snow can take on many forms.

Various types of snow form layers as storms pass by or the temperatures change in a single storm. As the snow piles up on the ground, the different layers can make it stable or unstable. Some piles of snow are so unstable that they slide downhill if anything disturbs them. A skier making tracks across the slope may be all that is needed to start an avalanche.

fluffy snow

icy snow

Figure 46a

The simplest conditions for an avalanche, and perhaps the least damaging, come when light, fluffy snow falls on top of hard, icy snow. The icy snow is smooth and slippery, as shown in Figure 46a. The fluffy snow does not stick and slides off. Because the fluffy snow is light, getting caught in an avalanche of this kind is less dangerous than other kinds. Sometimes strong skiers can literally ski out of this kiind of avalanche.

More dangerous conditions occur if light, fluffy snow falls on icy snow and then wet snow falls on the fluffy snow. The wet snow is heavy and may pull everything down. The heavy snow makes the avalanche much more dangerous.

The avalanches discussed above are the easiest to understand. However, a stable pile of snow can change into unstable snow. Temperature changes during the night and day make snow itself change. Although it sounds strange, even when the temperature is below freezing, water molecules can change into liquid water or even water vapor. Random collisions with other molecules in the ice crystal can give one molecule enough energy to break its bonds. For a brief time, the molecule is free to move.

Figure 46b

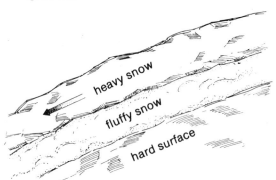

Molecules that are free to move tend to move upward through the snow layers and then refreeze someplace else. The lower layers of snow are made weaker because they lose molecules, while the upper layers get heavier. Eventually, the lower layer may become so weak that it cannot hold the rest of the snow layers. Often, large avalanches result because the weak layer is near the frozen ground, as shown in Figure 46b. Literally all the snow leaves the mountain slope.

One of the dangers of avalanches is that after the snow stops sliding, it quickly becomes very hard, like concrete. Anyone under the surface is frozen into this snow and it is very difficult to get that person out. This happens in the same way you make a snowball. When you press on the snow, a physicist would say that you are doing "work" on it. This work melts some snow at the edge of individual snow crystals. The snow quickly refreezes but the freezing joins crystals together. You have turned the soft snow into a solid snowball. Colder snow makes it harder to make a snowball because it is more difficult to melt the snow.

In an avalanche, large amounts of energy are released as the snow falls down the mountain. This energy melts lots of snow crystals. When the snow stops sliding it refreezes. The snow has been compressed so it becomes very dense, strong, and icy.

Review Questions

1) How does snow type affect the way avalanches form?

2) What happens to snow as the temperature changes?

3) How is making a snowball similar to what happens to snow in an avalanche?

How Everyday Things Work

TEACHER

Answers

1) Different types of snow have different densities and abilities to prevent sliding. If heavy snow falls on light snow, the pile of snow tends to be unstable.

2) As the temperature changes, snow melts and refreezes, sometimes on the molecular level and sometimes as the entire top layer. This changes the density and the strength of the snow. Those individual molecules that turn into a vapor tend to move upward, making the lower layers weaker and the upper layers heavier. This makes the pile unstable.

3) You do work on the snow that melts snow at the edges of the snow crystals. This refreezes and joins the crystals together. In avalanches, the gravitational potential energy is lost as the snow falls and melts snow crystals. The snow quickly becomes very hard after the snow stops moving.

The physics of avalanches is quite interesting. The following is a brief outline as to why they occur.

The first two types of avalanches discussed are relatively easy to understand. Too much weight falls on too slippery a surface. Down it goes. However, the third type of avalanche is a bit harder to understand.

The kinetic theory of matter says that all molecules are in constant motion and that through random collision some molecules may gain energy. A few molecules in the solid crystals may gain enough energy to break their solid bonds. The idea that individual water molecules can get enough energy to break their bonds and move may be a new idea for the students. When the molecules turn into a gas, they can travel. If they are in the liquid form, surface tension makes them form more spherical crystals. These more spherical crystals take up less space than the sharp, pointed crystals of new snow. They can start to act more like ball bearings than glue. The molecules that move in the snow quickly refreeze because the bulk of the snow is below freezing.

When an avalanche occurs, more ice at the surface of the crystals melts. The melted water solidifies and freezes the crystals together very quickly because the bulk of the snow is below freezing. The crystals are also made smaller because crystals are broken as they rub against each other. The avalanche snow becomes more compact, or dense, and freezes into an icy mass.

Your Sense of Taste and the Common Cold

When you have a cold, you can't taste your food. Everything tastes the same—sort of bland. The reason is that we do a lot of our tasting by smell. Taste buds in our mouths can identify some of the basic flavors: sweet, salty, bitter, and sour. Smell gives us other clues as to what we are eating. If your nose is stuffed up, you can't smell very well, so you can't taste your food. You can run an experiment to see how well you can taste things you can't smell—by eating things while holding your nose.

One problem with this experiment is that you may be able to identify foods by the way they feel in your mouth. Experiments are run so that you can test your hypothesis or "guess" about the results. You must make sure that the result occurs because of what you are testing and not for another reason. For instance, you should not compare carrots, cheese, and meat. You can easily tell which is which without even tasting them.

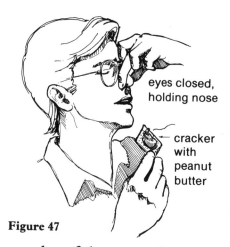

eyes closed, holding nose

← cracker with peanut butter

Figure 47

To run a controlled experiment about tasting, try eating the following things on crackers: peanut butter, cream cheese, and a thick onion dip. The idea is that each food should have approximately the same texture. They should also all be at the same temperature.

To run the experiment, prepare one cracker with each topping for every person in the group. Try to make each cracker have the same amount of topping. Then, close your eyes, hold your nose, and have another member of the group give you a cracker at random, as shown in Figure 47. Eat the cracker while holding your nose and try to identify which cracker you ate. Hold your nose until you have made your guess. Even after you swallow the cracker, you may still be able to smell what you ate.

How many of the crackers did you guess correctly? If you guessed correctly, did you identify the cracker because of some kind of taste or did you get a slight odor which told you?

TEACHER

Materials Needed

crackers	various toppings

This is a fun lab for students, although the results may not be as clear-cut as they would appear. One of the problems is that peanut butter is sweeter than cheese or dip, so students may be able to identify it because of sweetness. The other dips may be identified by texture. If you really want to run a controlled experiment, you may want to make three different flavored dips, all with the same base. The reason peanut butter, cream cheese, and thick dip are suggested is that these can be purchased in a store and have no preparation time.

Students should make sure that they put the same amount of dip on each cracker. They must also know which is which. (If you use three different flavors of dip, this is important.) Students must also also be honest about holding their breath and not looking. Although it will most likely not be a problem, you must also make sure that students don't put things which should not be eaten onto the crackers. Whenever people eat something they can't see or taste, there is always a danger of adulteration.

You may want to modify the lab so that some other odor is present when the students eat the crackers. If, for instance, a cracker with peanut butter is held right below the nose of someone eating another kind of cracker, the person may think he or she is eating peanut butter rather than the actual thing. Students may enjoy doing this. If you use the modification, it is possible to have the students not hold their noses but instead smell the food held below their noses.

48

Finding the Weight of a Bicycle or Car Using Tire Pressure

An interesting way to find the weight of a car is to use the air pressure in the tires. The same can be done with a bicycle or any other vehicle that uses tires filled with air. The only other materials you need are some graph paper, a meterstick, and a pressure gauge.

But how can you do it? Pressure is force per unit area. These units are often given as pounds per square inch (newtons per square meter in metric). By multiplying the pressure times area, you can find the force.

Find the weight of a bicycle and rider first. Later, you can find the weight of a car. First, with someone on the bicycle, measure the pressure of each tire with a pressure gauge. (Make sure that you don't let too much air out when you make the measurement.) Record these values. Then, roll the back wheel of the bicycle onto a piece of graph paper and draw an outline of the tire on the graph paper while a rider is sitting on the bike, as shown in Figure 48. Label this "the back wheel" and include the tire pressure. Repeat this procedure for the front wheel. (Note: Knobby tires give less accurate values.)

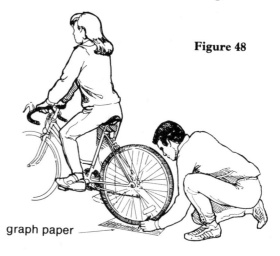

Figure 48

graph paper

Now, take the graph paper and count how many squares are enclosed in the outline of each wheel. Count carefully, to get as accurate a value for the area as possible. Record this value on your graph paper. Next, find the area of one square with the meterstick. If you are using pounds per square inch, find the area in inches. If you are using newtons per square meter, find the number of square meters.

How Everyday Things Work

Finally, use the equation below to find the weight on each tire. Remember to use the pressure and area for the front tire and then pressure and area for the back tire. Add the weights to find the total weight. How does it compare to the weight of the rider plus bicycle? The equation for finding weight is:

weight = (number of squares) $\times$ (area of square) $\times$ (pressure)

You can repeat this experiment for a car or a truck. Find your values safely and also don't let too much air out of the tires when you find the pressure. Remember, you have to find the area and pressure for all four tires.

TEACHER

Materials Needed

graph paper   pressure gauge
meterstick   bicycle and/or car

This interesting experiment can give rather good results. The main problem is that the tire tread must be relatively smooth. If knobby tires are used, then you have to estimate how much of the tread really is exerting pressure on the ground. The equipment is simple and graph paper is the only expendable material.

Pressure gauges in the United States generally give values in pounds per square inch which may, therefore, be the units of choice for this experiment (although science students should learn the metric system). One conversion factor you might need to use if the pressure reads in atmospheres is: 1 atmosphere equals 100,000 newtons per square meter. There are about .22 pounds per newton.

Because of problems finding the area, the lab may give values that are 10% off from the actual value of the weight of the bicycle and rider. The results have approximately the same accuracy when you find the weight of a car.

When finding the area, different types of graph paper require different methods of counting squares. If the graph paper has large squares, then in order to get a good value for area, you need to count fractions of squares. With smaller squares, you can direct the students to count more than half a square as a whole square and less than half a square as nothing. If the graph paper has small squares, it may help the students to outline rectangles of smaller squares and calculate the number of squares inside the outline. Then they can count the number of squares outside the outlined rectangles. It may also help to find the area of a number of squares with the meterstick rather than just one. Students can then say that 10 or 100 squares have an area of _____ , so 1 square has an area of _____ .

Students must realize that if they let too much air out of a tire, they will have to pump it up again. It may be helpful to have a pump available for this reason.

49

Suction Cups

Suction cups are interesting little things. Who would think that a rubber cup pressed on a smooth surface would stick? Sometimes they unstick quickly, like the suction cups on dart gun darts. Others, like the ones you stick on a window to hold a thermometer or bird feeder, seem to stick forever. But what holds them on the surface?

Actually, two physics principles are involved: friction and air pressure. Friction keeps the suction cup from sliding down the surface and air pressure keeps it against the surface. When the suction cup is on the wall, gravity tries to pull it down. An upward force must oppose gravity or the suction cup will fall. Friction opposes motion between two surfaces. The cup would slide along the wall, so a frictional force opposes the fall.

In order to have a frictional force, you need a force perpendicular, or at right angles, to the wall. This force is provided by air pressure. The suction cup is designed so that when it is pressed against a smooth surface, air is squeezed out of the cup. The suction cup is smooth and can fill any microscopic holes with its squishy rubber. It prevents air from coming back into the cup.

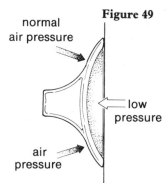

Figure 49

normal air pressure

low pressure

air pressure

The cup is also springy. Once it has been pushed, it wants to return to its original shape. Because air has been squeezed out of the cup, the cup makes a partial vacuum. The pressure in the cup is less than the pressure of the air outside. Because the pressure is greater outside the cup than inside, a force pushes on the cup to keep it against the wall. This is a force at right angles to the wall, which is needed for friction. This is shown in Figure 49.

After a time, most suction cups fall off because air gets into them. This increases the pressure inside. Eventually, the cup isn't forced against the wall hard enough by the outside air, so friction can't hold it up. Better quality rubber in the suction cups tends to keep the air out longer so the suction cups stick longer.

How Everyday Things Work

Review Questions

1) What two things keep a suction cup on the wall?

2) What force opposes gravity?

3) Why is the suction cup held against the wall?

4) What keeps some suction cups up longer than others?

How Everyday Things Work

┌─────────────────┐
│ **TEACHER**   │
└─────────────────┘

Answers

1) Frictional force prevents the cup from sliding down and air pressure keeps it pushed against the wall.

2) Friction opposes gravity, which would make the cup slide down the wall. Friction always opposes motion between two surfaces.

3) The pressure inside the suction cup is smaller than it is outside. This produces a net force to make the suction cup stick. The partial vacuum in the suction cup occurs because air is pushed out and then the cup wants to return to its original shape.

4) If air gets into the cup, it falls. Some cups are made of rubber, which fills small holes in the surface and prevents air from entering. These stay up longer.

Suction cups are quite familiar to most people, but often the reason why they stick is unknown. Suction cups stick because the pressure difference between the outside and inside causes a force that pushes the cup against the wall. This force then supplies the perpendicular force needed to cause friction. If there is no force between two surfaces, there can be no frictional force.

The characteristics of the rubber allow the suction cup to stick. It must force air out when pushed against the wall and not allow it back in when released. Soft rubber can do this well. The rubber also needs to spring back. If the cup did not spring back, it would not cause the partial vacuum. The air is squeezed out and then the cup returns to its original size without letting more air in. Because the number of molecules in the cup is less than before, fewer collisions occur within the cup, so the pressure is less ($PV = nRT$). When the number of molecules, n, is smaller, so is the pressure, P.

Friction prevents the cup from sliding. The difference in air pressure provides the perpendicular (or normal) force to cause friction. Because rubber has a relatively high coefficient of friction, or resistance to slipping, it sticks quite well. (A balloon rubbed on your hair sticks on the wall because of friction, but in that case the perpendicular force is provided by electrical attraction.)

50
How Carbonated Drinks Are Made

Many drinks are carbonated; when you open them, they fizz or foam. The bubbles that produce the fizz and foam are caused by carbon dioxide trapped in the liquid. But how does the gas get there? Why does it come out?

Carbon dioxide dissolves in water, which is the main ingredient in soft drinks, beer, and sparkling wines. However, more carbon dioxide can be dissolved, or "put into the solution," when the pressure is high. When the top is taken off, the pressure in a can or bottle is reduced so carbon dioxide starts coming out of the water.

Carbon dioxide is put into solution in two ways. The first puts high-pressure carbon dioxide in a container of water. If carbon dioxide bubbles out of solution when the pressure is released, it goes into solution when pressure is increased. The second method uses carbon dioxide produced in a natural fermentation process. Beer and sparkling wines are capped to retain this carbon dioxide.

Carbon dioxide comes out of solution faster when it is shaken or disturbed. It is also helped out of solution when it touches a surface like an ice cube or a glass. This is why pouring a soda into a glass of ice makes lots of foam.

You can run an experiment to see how much carbon dioxide a bottle of soda has. Fill a large transparent container with water and cover the top of it with your hand. Turn the container over into a large bowl holding a small amount of water. The water should stay in the container. Have your partner hold the container so it doesn't tip.

Now, take a bottle of soda and very carefully remove the top. Pour half the soda out into a clean paper cup. (You can drink this later.) Then, gently slide a rubber tube over the mouth of the bottle and run the tube so it goes up into the container of water, as shown in Figure 50.

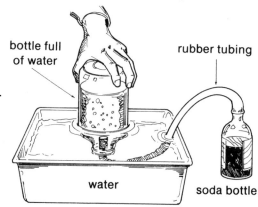

Figure 50

How Everyday Things Work

Now shake the bottle gently. You don't want liquid to come out the top, just gas. How much carbon dioxide has come out? Pour the soda in the bottle into another clean cup and compare the taste of the soda with and without carbonation.

WARNING: Do not taste any of the soda if the equipment you are using has been used for chemistry experiments.

TEACHER

Materials Needed

bottle(s) of soda	rubber tubing
clean, empty liter bottle	water
bowl or pan	cups

This experiment can be done quite easily and is fun for students. One possible danger is associated with the rubber tubing. It is best to have tubing that is used **only** for this experiment and then either stored with proper labeling until the following year or thrown away.

WARNING: This **tubing must be clean** and never have been involved in chemistry experiments **of any kind.**

The tubing can be obtained from medical supply stores or through chemical supply houses. It must be of large enough diameter that it can slide over the neck of a bottle. This size tubing is expensive, so you may want to do this experiment as a demonstration. An alternative is to run the experiment using chemical glassware from a chemistry lab. One-holed stoppers can be put on flasks where the soda is placed.

WARNING: If chemistry lab apparatus is used, students should not be allowed to taste any of the soda.

The container to collect the gas must hold about a quart of water; two-liter soda bottles work well. A translucent plastic milk container could also be used. Remember, the bowl in which the container of water is held must be able to contain the water initially poured into it plus the water that is expelled from the inverted container. If you are going to have the students drink the soda, the container and the bowl must **NEVER** have been used in chemistry experiments.

The amount of carbon dioxide that comes out of solution depends on the original pressure and on the temperature. The pressure in soda, sparkling wine, and beer is maintained by the cap. In fermentation processes where carbonation is not desired, the carbon dioxide from fermentation is released into the air through a vapor lock. It allows the gases to escape but does not allow air to come in.

51
How Baking Soda Works

Baking soda causes cakes or cookies to rise. If you forget to add the baking soda when mixing your ingredients, nothing rises and you have a flat cake or cookie. But how does the baking soda do it?

Baking soda is an interesting substance. It is a "base," which means that it is the opposite of an "acid." It is made of sodium and carbon dioxide bonded together.

When baking soda is heated, carbon dioxide is released. Because carbon dioxide is a gas, it makes bubbles in the cookies or cakes. The gas takes up space so the cookies or cakes rise. The cookie dough or cake batter then becomes harder around these bubbles as the cooking takes place, as shown in Figure 51a. This hardening prevents the cookie or cake from "falling." A cake falls if it is not cooked long enough and the walls surrounding the bubbles are not firm enough to hold up its weight.

Figure 51a

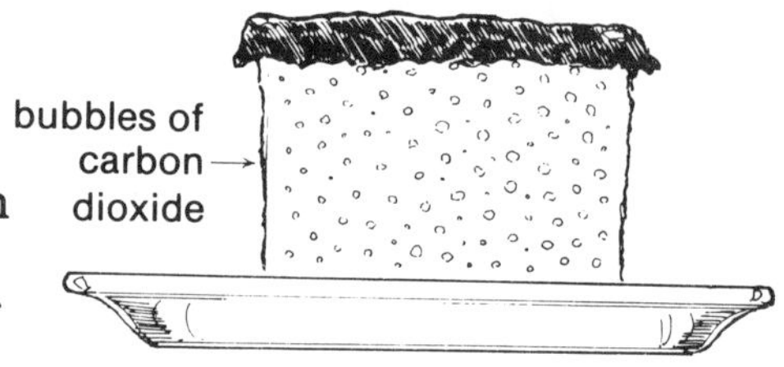

bubbles of carbon dioxide →

cake

Yeast also produces carbon dioxide as it grows. Yeast is made up of actual living organisms that are used in bread-making because they also make carbon dioxide.

You can experiment to see how carbon dioxide is released from baking soda. You can release the carbon dioxide by adding a weak acid, like vinegar, instead of heating the baking soda as is done in baking. Fill a large bowl or pan with about two cups of water. Add a tablespoon of vinegar and mix it thoroughly. Then take a teaspoon of baking soda and sprinkle it on the surface. What happens? What happens if you use more vinegar or more baking soda? What gas must you be releasing in this chemical reaction?

TEACHER

Materials Needed

bucket	baking soda
beaker	vinegar
water	rubber tube

Optional: soda bottle, plastic wrap

This experiment can be a bit messy, so be careful. You should run it beforehand so you know how much baking soda and vinegar to use with your particular apparatus.

The amount of carbon dioxide released is related to the amounts of baking soda and vinegar. Smaller amounts of baking soda cause less gas to be given off. Less vinegar means that some of the baking soda doesn't react and give off its carbon dioxide.

If you want students to find the actual amount of carbon dioxide given off from a specific amount of baking soda, you can collect the gas and measure its volume. It is best to do this alternate experiment with smaller amounts and to use beakers with volumes marked on them. Fill a bucket with water. Then, fill a beaker with water and invert it with the mouth under water so the beaker remains full of water. If you put a measured amount of baking soda in a test tube and then add vinegar, the gas can be collected by connecting a rubber tube that expels the gas to the bottom of the inverted beaker. The volume of gas can then be read off the beaker.

This experiment can be done with separate groups using different amounts of baking soda in their test tubes. The groups can then compare the amounts of gas they get to see if more baking soda produces more gas.

You can also do a more dramatic experiment using a soda bottle. Place a teaspoon of vinegar in the bottle and add water so the bottle is about ¾ full.

plastic wrap enclosing baking soda

water and vinegar

Figure 51b

Now, make a small pouch with some plastic wrap and place a teaspoon of baking soda in it. Twist the plastic wrap so it holds the baking soda but will also be able to fit into the bottle. Put your baking soda pouch in the bottle carefully so the baking soda doesn't come in contact with the vinegar water, as shown in Figure 51b. When you are in a place where you will not make a mess, most likely outside, shake the bottle. The carbon dioxide will push the water out of the bottle in the same way that carbon dioxide fire extinguishers work.

WARNING: DO NOT POINT THE BOTTLE AT ANYONE.

Although the ingredients are not dangerous, the spray should be kept out of eyes and off clothes. It is also possible to build up enough pressure to break the bottle if it is capped. If students do the experiment on their own at home, they may not use strong enough containers. Students should be discouraged from running this experiment on their own.

52

Acid Rain

People talk about acid rain and how it is bad for the environment. Like many issues, this one is not clear-cut. Some evidence says acid rain causes serious harm, some suggests that it causes no real damage. Scientists disagree, but this kind of disagreement keeps science alive and exciting.

A scientific scale indicates whether something is an *acid* or a *base* (sort of the opposite of acid). This scale is called the *pH scale*. A neutral substance (neither an acid nor a base) has a pH of 7. Strong acids have a pH of 1; strong bases have a pH of 14. A difference of 1 on the pH scale means that something is 10 times more acidic or basic. If the pH differs by 2, it is 100 times more acidic or basic ($10 \times 10 = 100$). The lower the pH, the more acidic the substance.

Rain has been acidic since the dawn of time. As water forms drops in the atmosphere, it combines with carbon dioxide in the air. Carbon dioxide and water form carbonic acid. This causes a raindrop to naturally have a pH of about 5.4 This is not neutral (pH = 7); it is slightly acidic.

"Acid rain" occurs as sulfur and nitrogen oxides combine with the raindrops. These gases get into the air from burning fuels. The nitric and sulfur oxides combine with water to form strong nitric and sulfuric acids. Rain has been observed to have a pH of 3 or less. This is as acidic as vinegar. These strong acids can cause problems in plants and animals.

Figure 52

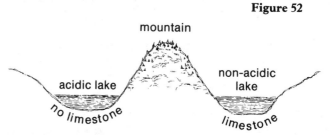

In many places, however, the soils and rocks of an area contain substances like limestone that neutralize the acid rain, as shown in Figure 52. Problems associated with acid rain occur mostly in areas with no limestone in the soil. In some cases, it has been possible to reverse the effects of acid rain in a lake by adding limestone to it. The limestone neutralizes acid, so no damage occurs.

Acid causes problems in lakes because it prevents animals such as fish, salamanders, and insects from reproducing or surviving. Fish suffer the most because they cannot reproduce and lose food sources. Some acid lakes have lost all their fish. These lakes tend to be crystal clear because nothing grows in them to make the water cloudy. It startles many people to think that these pure looking lakes are actually devoid of life.

On land, acid rain affects plants and trees. The acid makes some chemicals leave the soil so the plants can't get enough food into their roots. Other chemicals that are toxic to the plants are released by the acid. One chemical in particular, aluminum, causes severe problems. Acidic soils make aluminum dissolve. It kills trees and other plants when it enters their roots. Some trees and plant species are hurt more than others, but in any case the acid stresses them.

Acid rain also affects structures. The acid causes metal in bridges and cars to rust faster. It causes paint to decay faster, which means that houses must be painted more often. It even affects the paint on cars, which can become pitted by acid rain. Marble statues and buildings also suffer because marble dissolves, releasing carbon dioxide, when acid comes in contact with it. Some marble buildings literally fizz in particularly acidic rain.

Some scientists dispute whether acid rain causes all the problems that have just been discussed. Ozone is responsible for at least some of the problems trees and plants experience. While ozone in the upper atmosphere blocks out ultraviolet light, ozone at ground level is toxic. Ozone is created by industry and by burning fuels. Other scientists point out that acid comes from other sources, including such things as mosses. Most scientists agree that acid rain causes added stress. When the plants are further stressed with a drought or insect attack, they die because they are already weak.

Scientists are studying acid rain with the hope that they can understand the extent of damage it causes. The more we know about acid rain, the better equipped we will be to deal with it.

Review Questions

1) What are acid rain sources and how can they be reduced?

2) What is acid rain and why is it a problem?

3) What does an acid rain lake look like and why?

4) When does acid rain not cause problems in lakes?

TEACHER

Answers

1) Reducing the burning of fossil fuels or making them burn more cleanly reduces acid rain. The nitrogen and sulfur oxides in flue gases from power plants and the exhaust from cars are the main sources of acid rain. Scrubbers are used on power plants to trap particles and gases before they leave the power plant. The catalytic converters in cars do much the same thing. Some acids are added to the atmosphere from natural sources such as volcanoes, but these are not normally a large source.

2) Rain that is more acidic than the normal pH of 5.4 is considered "acid rain." Carbonic acid gives rain a pH of 5.4. Recall that a pH of 4.4 would be 10 times more acidic, so a pH of 3 (which has been recorded in many places) puts the rain more than 100 times more acidic than normal. The acid itself is toxic to organisms or it releases toxic substances into the soil or water or it causes corrosion or decay of paint, metal, and marble.

3) Lakes that have become completely acidic naturally look clear blue. They have no life in them to make them murky. Algae and other life forms cannot live, so the water is clear.

4) Acid rain is not a problem in areas with limestone in the soil. The limestone neutralizes acid rain quickly. The areas with acid rain problems tend to be mountainous areas with thin soils and igneous rocks like granite. The rock of the northeastern mountains and eastern Canada is of this type, so acid rain affects these areas.

Acid rain is not a simple problem. Experts disagree on how large a problem it is. Some research points one way, some the other. The effects of smog seem to add to the complexity.

A few examples of the problems associated with showing the true damage caused by acid rain might be interesting to discuss with the students. For example, some researchers have indicated that whole species are dying as a result of acid rain. Red spruce forests, which are sensitive to acid rain, seem to be declining in the northeastern U.S. But they are not the climax species; other trees will eventually replace them. Should we then be concerned that acid rain may speed the spruce forests' decline, or should we simply accept the fact that they were going to die anyway?

Another example involves sphagnum moss. This moss grows slowly in cool, moist areas. Some research says that it is killing trees because it releases acids in order to get nutrients. Because it has no root system, it must release a great amount of acid to the area around it to get food. As the forests age, the ground becomes more shaded. This leads to cooler temperatures and more moisture. Slowly the mosses and their acid build up, and this acid—not acid rain—kills the trees around them. Acids from both pollution and nature can kill trees. Which one is to blame, the moss or the polluting factories? The answer isn't completely clear.

53

How Cars Are Made Fuel-Efficient

Making cars more fuel-efficient saves natural resources, reduces pollution and carbon dioxide emissions, and saves drivers money. But how can cars be made more fuel-efficient? What can manufacturers do that hasn't already been done? A number of areas are being investigated, but four of the main ones are *engine efficiency, reduction of weight, tire design,* and *streamlining.*

The engine burns gasoline. The more rapidly it burns, the larger the pressure that builds up in the cylinders. With more pressure, the engine exerts more force. With more force from a given amount of gasoline, the car can go farther on a gallon of gas. Using two spark plugs instead of one makes the fuel start burning in two places instead of one. This causes it to burn more uniformly and more quickly and increases the pressure.

Engineers are also looking at how the gasoline and the air needed to burn it get into the cylinders. If more air (and more oxygen) are in the cylinders, then the burning is more complete. This is what turbochargers do. They put compressed air into the cylinders, which helps make all the gasoline burn. One problem with this system is that the cylinders run at a higher temperature, so the cylinders and other parts wear faster.

Engineers have also changed the way fuel is put into the cylinders. Fuel-injection systems squirt gas directly into the cylinder instead of mixing it with air in a carburetor. The fuel injectors allow more efficient operation because the fuel can be added in precisely the correct amount by a computer. Less gas is wasted, so the car runs more efficiently.

Reducing the weight of cars also increases mileage. When metal parts are replaced with plastic or lightweight materials, the mass of the car is reduced. With less mass, less energy has to be given to the car to get it going at a given velocity. (Kinetic energy, or energy of motion, is given by the equation: $K.E. = \frac{1}{2}mv^2$.) Reducing weight reduces friction because frictional force is related to the force between two surfaces. With less weight, frictional forces between the car and the axles are reduced.

How Everyday Things Work

Tire design is also being investigated for fuel savings. Radial tires are now used on most cars because they roll with much less friction due to the way they are built. But other changes may be made, too. Tread design may make tires roll slightly more efficiently, but changing the air pressure does much more. Using more pressure in tires makes them roll more easily because less tire is in contact with the road, as shown in Figure 53a. One problem with greater pressure in the tires is that it makes a rougher ride. You may have experienced this when your bicycle tires are underinflated. It is harder to pedal, but the bumps don't bother you as much.

Figure 53a

harder to roll   easier to roll

Figure 53b

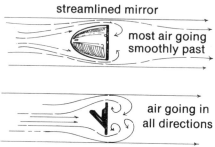

streamlined mirror

most air going smoothly past

air going in all directions

non-streamlined mirror

Streamlining cars has helped them to run more efficiently, but most of the gains in this area have already been realized. Mirrors, lights, and windshield wipers are being made so air moves over them smoothly, as shown in Figure 53b. The place where the largest improvements can now be made is the bottom of the car. If the bottom were completely smooth, with no holes or compartments, air friction would be reduced. However, if the bottom is sealed, it is difficult to work on the car. An easy way to reduce air friction is to drive more slowly. As long as you are in the top gear and your engine is running smoothly, your car is operating more efficiently when driven more slowly.

Review Questions

1) How can engines be made more energy-efficient?

2) How does weight affect fuel economy, and why?

3) How can tires be made to roll with less friction?

4) When driving a car, how can you reduce air friction to save energy?

5) Try to think of some other things that might be done to save energy as you drive.

TEACHER

Answers

1) Engines can use more than one spark plug, put more air in the cylinders, or use fuel injectors to make the fuel burn more efficiently.

2) Reducing weight reduces the amount of kinetic energy a car needs to go at a given speed. It also reduces frictional forces.

3) Better tread design and higher prressure can make tires roll more easily, which saves fuel.

4) By reducing your speed, which reduces friction.

5) This is an open-ended question and students may not have answers to this. Some suggestions are given below.

Many students tend to be interested in cars, and making cars more efficient will be important for future generations. The four main areas outlined in this chapter seem to be the most advantageous.

However, engine efficiency can be improved in a few other ways. Some car companies are looking at literally turning off the engine whenever possible. The engine would be stopped when at a stoplight or even when going downhill. It would then be automatically restarted using a flywheel which kept spinning. The problem with this type of system is that it must be reliable. Other methods include using different materials in the engines and different ignition systems. Some changes make cars both more fuel-efficient and more reliable. The electronic ignitions used now are beneficial because they make a hotter spark in the spark plug, which does a better job of igniting the gasoline, and they are also less likely to need repair.

Reducing the weight of cars has focused on making the cars smaller and using more and more parts made out of plastic or composite materials. One problem with smaller, lighter cars is that they can incur more damage in a collision. The people inside then have a much higher chance of injury or death. Rear-engine cars are now rare because an engine, with all its mass, helps prevent deaths in front-end collisions, the kind that occur most frequently. Plastics can be made as strong as steel. Fenders and other parts are slowly changing to plastic materials, but some metal parts are hard to replace. The main reason behind using small spare tires is also to reduce weight.

Radial tires improve fuel economy and tread design can also help. Snow tires, for instance, are less fuel-efficient than regular tires. Increasing the pressure of the tires can save the most energy, but it will make the ride less smooth. With greater pressure in the tires, they absorb fewer bumps. Redesigning the shock absorbers and springs may solve this problem.

Streamlining cars continues to help, but cars must still fit people comfortably. You may want to have students look at the angles of the hoods and windshields of cars in a parking lot. The angles of most cars' front hoods are similar because that angle is the most efficient in wind tunnel tests.

54

How Do Bug Repellents Work?

Biting insects are a problem. But how do bug repellents keep the little beasties away? The theory of how bug repellents work is not actually complete, but a few ideas do seem to explain what happens.

Most work has been done with mosquitoes because they are a problem everywhere the temperatures go above freezing. The way mosquitoes find warm-blooded animals is quite interesting, and seems to be the key to preventing mosquitoes from biting.

Scientists have found that mosquitoes become more active when the concentration of carbon dioxide (CO_2) increases. Mosquitoes have been studied in screened cages. Normally, with 100 mosquitoes in the cage, 5 or 10 might be flying. When CO_2 is released into the cage, many more take to the air. This behavior helps them find prey because warm-blooded animals exhale CO_2. Mosquitoes start flying when dinner walks past.

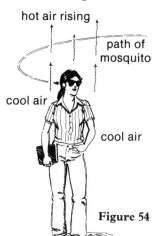

hot air rising

path of mosquito

cool air

cool air

Figure 54

Once they start flying, they use heat rising off the warm-blooded animal to zoom in on a meal. Mosquitoes are programmed so when they fly from cool to warm air, they keep flying but drop down lower. By dropping down, they move closer to the source of the warm air rising from an animal. When mosquitoes fly from warm air into cold, they turn around, as shown in Figure 54. This keeps them near their warm-blooded meal.

Some insect repellents seem to take advantage of the way the mosquitoes change direction when air temperatures change. The chemicals seem to block the ability of the mosquito to sense the change in temperature. The mosquito

How Everyday Things Work

just flies away. The blocking action comes from the molecules that evaporate from the skin. These molecules enter the insect's sensing system and confuse it. A few molecules seem to be able to stop the bug from finding you. This means that a relatively small amount of repellent is needed to keep the bugs from biting.

Review Questions

1) What tends to get mosquitoes flying instead of sitting?

2) How does a mosquito find its dinner once in the air?

3) What is the theory as to how some bug repellents work?

TEACHER

Answers

1) CO_2 seems to make mosquitoes fly instead of sit. It is produced by warm-blooded animals when they breathe.

2) The mosquito drops down when flying into warm air and turns around when flying into cold air. This results in the mosquito getting closer and closer to its meal.

3) Bug repellents may block the temperature sensor on the mosquito, making it impossible to find the prey. They just keep flying.

The chemicals used to keep bugs away are varied. Some seem to be more effective than others. Some of the old-fashioned repellents seem to work relatively well, but the newer ones are more effective and can be used in much smaller amounts.

The most effective chemical seems to be N,N diethylmetatoluamide. It is possible that this chemical is harmful to the people it protects, but tests have not shown this to be so. Some doctors recommend that small children, whose skin is more permeable than adult skin, should not use this repellent. The chemical also melts plastic and takes off varnish, so one might wonder what it does to humans. This ingredient is in virtually all insect repellents on the market.

Other chemicals have not been studied as much, but one product, Skin-So-Soft™, seems to keep bugs away. The active ingredient has not been identified and it may be a combination of chemicals. It is not as effective as some other products, but it works if applied regularly.

Old-fashioned insect repellents seem to make the bugs move away because of a noxious smell. Citronella is effective but seems to work in much the same way that smoke does. Bugs avoid it. One old-time formula uses pine tar. A high school biologist once suggested to me that "With that stuff on, you smell like a creosote telephone pole. Bugs know they can't eat them. . . ."

One of the amazing things about N,N diethylmetatoluamide is that it works on a wide range of bugs. It seems to repel ticks and chiggers, as well as mosquitoes and black flies. This probably has to do with the fact that all these bugs have rather simple nervous systems. If the chemical works to confuse one bug, it probably does the same for others.

55

How Does Smog Form?

Smog is a global problem. But what causes it and how can it be prevented? Why is it worse in some places than in others?

Smog is associated with air pollution and is not like haze, which is the natural water vapor in the air. The water vapor scatters sunlight traveling through it, so you can't see long distances. The Great Smoky Mountains were named because of this kind of haze, perhaps with some forest fire smoke mixed in.

Smog is caused by polluted air from a variety of sources. Power plants, chemical plants, automobiles and trucks, open fires, dry cleaning stores, and spray paints all add to air pollution. Their contributions to the air reduce visibility and people suffer health effects.

Polluted air changes as it is exposed to sunlight. When the ultraviolet rays in sunlight strike polluted air, photochemical reactions take place. Photochemical reactions occur when light, which is made of photons, reacts with the chemicals in the polluted air. The chemicals often become worse than the initial pollution. The air can be cleaned when it rains, because the chemicals in the smog often attach to the raindrops that fall to the ground.

The amount of pollution in an area is related to its weather and its geography. Sunny days with light winds are the worst. The photochemical reactions occur and then the smog stays. A good rainstorm followed by winds clears the air and gets rid of the smog. When storms don't occur often enough, the air can become very polluted with smog.

Cities along the east coast of the United States have problems with smog. Part of the problem is that each city adds a little more pollution to the air, which then drifts to the next city. As the air drifts, sunlight changes the chemicals and makes things worse. Because the winds tend to move up the east coast, a band of polluted air often stretches north from Washington, D.C. to Boston.

Another place with serious smog problems is in southern California. This area has a very dry climate, so the air isn't cleaned very often by rain. The coastal cities are backed by mountains, which are rather close to the ocean. The mountains trap the air over these cities and new, clean air doesn't replace the polluted air, as shown in Figure 55. Because of all the sunny days, the photochemical smog in this area is often the worst in the country.

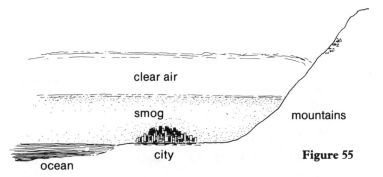

Figure 55

Smog can be lessened by reducing the amount of pollution that enters the air. Pollution can be reduced by cleaning the gases that leave smokestacks, using special devices on cars, trapping escaping gases from gasoline pumps, and reducing the amounts of all kinds of human-made gases that enter the air.

Southern California has some of the strictest pollution controls. People drive cars that have superior pollution-control devices, they don't burn leaves or charcoal in barbeques, they have special devices on gas-pump nozzles, they use the latest technology in their power plants, and they strictly control the release of gases from chemical companies. Even with all these controls, they still have many days with unhealthful air.

Other places, such as Denver, have troubles too. The Rocky Mountains to the west tend to trap air over Denver, so the smog is not cleared away. Smog is even found in the Arctic because of oil drilling operations and other industrial activities.

Review Questions

1) What is the difference between smog and haze?

2) What is a photochemical reaction?

3) What gets rid of smog from the air?

4) Why are many cities along the east coast subject to smog?

5) What causes the bad smog conditions in southern California?

6) What can be done to prevent smog from forming?

TEACHER

Answers

1) Smog is associated with polluted air; haze is water vapor mixed, perhaps, with some forest fire smoke.

2) Photochemical reactions occur as ultraviolet rays in sunlight cause chemical reactions in the polluted air. Ultraviolet light has enough energy to break bonds.

3) Rain and wind clear smog from the air.

4) East coast cities often have winds that blow the smog northeast along the coast. Pollution from one city is passed along to the next, adding more pollution for the next city.

5) The mountains tend to trap the air between them and the ocean, so the air is never completely cleaned. They also have little air-cleansing rain for most of the year, and lots of sunshine that causes photochemical reactions.

6) Reducing pollution is the only way we have at present to reduce smog.

Smog and air pollution go hand in hand. Some cities have worse problems than others because of their local geography. The actual chemical changes that occur as smog forms are quite complex, although they are known in their basic form by scientists working in the field.

Hydrocarbons are a real problem in that they often change from one chemical form to another by photochemical reactions. Hydrocarbons are found in fuels, dry cleaning materials, and chemicals used in industry. Reducing the amount of these gases that is released into the atmosphere reduces smog.

Some sources of smog are hard to control. One major source of pollution is fires. A large fire can cause pollution over huge areas of the country. The smoke is made of partially burned hydrocarbons and these, like most hydrocarbons, react photochemically. The forest fires in Yellowstone National Park in 1989 and the oil well fires in Kuwait in 1991 are examples of wide-ranging air pollution. Eventually, the pollutants are washed from the air by rain. If the area is dry, however, the process takes a long time.

56

How Air Pollution
Is Reduced at Power Plants

A major source of air pollution is the generation of electricity in large coal-burning power plants. But how have these pollution sources been made less polluting? How have scientists and engineers gotten rid of the smoke and other gases and helped the environment? What are the problems associated with these pollution controls?

When coal is burned, it releases gases and particles that cause air pollution. Coal is mostly carbon and hydrogen. When carbon and hydrogen are burned, they produce carbon dioxide and water. These gases don't cause pollution, although carbon dioxide can cause global warming. The pollution problem is caused by impurities in the coal. Coal is not pure carbon and hydrogen.

Sulfur, minerals, and other chemicals are some of the impurities in coal. Coal is formed from plants that were compressed, heated, and then changed into a solid. Because plants contain other chemicals besides carbon and hydrogen, coal will have small amounts of these other chemicals as well. These impurities cause pollution. Sulfur in the coal, when burned, combines with oxygen to form sulfur oxides. These combine with water in the air to form sulfuric acid. Small mineral particles make soot and dirty the air. Also, as the coal burns, the high temperatures cause nitrogen in the air to combine with oxygen to form nitric oxides. As with the sulfur oxides, nitric oxides combine with water drops in the air and form nitric acid.

It is obviously not good to have nitric acid and sulfuric acid in the air. It is also bad to have the particles of smoke escape from the smokestack because they cause pollution and reduce visibility. This is why power companies clean the gases produced by the burning coal before the smoke is released into the atmosphere.

Two methods are often used to clean the gases: *electrostatic precipitators* and *scrubbers*. Electrostatic precipitators use static electricity to remove particles from the smoke. Scrubbers spray water containing chemicals that combine with the sulfur and nitric oxides in the smoke. The pollutants are captured before they escape into the air.

 How Everyday Things Work

An electrostatic precipitator uses electrically-charged plates to attract the soot before it leaves the power plant, as shown in Figure 56a. The charged plates attract the small soot particles in the same way that a comb rubbed on your head attracts small bits of dust. After the soot is attracted to the charged plates, the plates are discharged and shaken to collect the soot. The process can be noisy but can remove more than 90% of the soot particles from the smoke.

You can run an experiment to see how electrostatic forces can affect small objects. Rub a comb through your hair and then bring it near, but don't touch, a small stream of water from a faucet. The water drops move in strange ways.

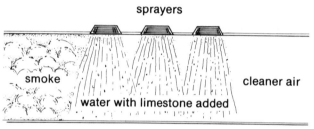

Figure 56a

Figure 56b

A scrubber sprays water and limestone into the smoke to get rid of the sulfur and nitric oxides that can turn into acids in the air, as shown in Figure 56b. Limestone reacts with the sulfur and nitric oxides and turns them into less-damaging chemicals, which are collected and moved to a landfill. The scrubber makes the gases react in the scrubber rather than after escaaping into the atmosphere.

There are problems with electrostatic precipitators and scrubbers. They are expensive, they require large amounts of energy to operate, and they produce wastes that must be disposed of. All this is costly, so pollution controls add to the expense of building a power plant. The added costs make the electricity produced by these plants cost more. The benefit is that these pieces of equipment reduce damage to the environment.

Review Questions

1) Why does burning coal produce pollution?

2) How does an electrostatic precipitator work?

3) How does a scrubber work in a power plant?

4) What are the costs of pollution controls for power plants? What are the benefits?

TEACHER

Answers

1) Coal contains impurities from the plants that formed it. These impurities are released either as particles or as chemicals.

2) An electrostatic precipitator uses charged plates to attract the small soot particles in smoke. It works much the same way that a comb charged by rubbing on your hair attracts dust.

3) Scrubbers spray water with chemicals, such as limestone (calcium carbonate), into the exhaust gases. This causes a chemical reaction with the nitric and sulfur dioxides that removes them from the air as solids.

4) The machinery costs money, it takes energy to operate, and the trapped pollutants need to be put in a landfill. The benefits are that the pollutants are kept in one place and are not spread over the countryside. Also, fewer chemicals are released into the atmosphere.

Burning coal produces pollution that must be cleaned up before it leaves a power plant. In the early 1900's dirty air was a sign of progress, and people were proud of their blackened skies. However, times have changed and we now know that pollution is more than just a minor irritation—it is dangerous to health and to the environment.

The technology to clean up power plants is expensive, although it is less expensive to design new plants to be clean than to retrofit old plants. For this reason, pollution controls are stricter for new plants than for older ones.

The technology of pollution control is more complex than described in the student section. The general outline of how electrostatic precipitators and scrubbers work is correct, but the actual methods may vary from plant to plant. Pollution can be reduced by making the coal burn more cleanly to start with. The pollutants are literally removed from the coal before it is burned. Fluidized bed combustion allows for better combustion and production of fewer nitric oxides. Some systems clean the sulfur from coal before burning it, which reduces this form of pollution.

The charged plates of the electrostatic precipitators attract the soot particles because the particles become polarized. If the plate is positive, the positive charges in the soot move away from the plate while the negative charges in the soot move toward the plate. The soot particles move toward the plate and become stuck. When enough particles are on the plates, the plates are discharged and then shaken. The soot particles form in larger chunks and fall to where they are collected.

The energy needed to run the pollution control devices can take up to 10% of the energy used by the power plant. This means that the power plant runs less efficiently and produces more carbon dioxide for each kilowatt-hour of electricity produced.

57

Ozone: Good and Bad?

ozone   normal
         oxygen

Figure 57a

Ozone is an interesting chemical. An ozone molecule is made with three atoms of oxygen bonded together. The oxygen molecule we use when we breathe is made of two oxygen atoms bonded together, as shown in Figure 57a. These different molecules behave very differently.

Ozone in the upper atmosphere absorbs ultraviolet radiation, which can cause skin cancer and damage plants. Normal oxygen molecules with two atoms cannot do this. However, when you breathe ozone, the ozone can damage your lungs because it reacts chemically with cells in your lungs. It is interesting that a molecule is helpful in some places and damaging in others.

Normally, ozone in the upper atmosphere is made at a constant rate equal to the rate at which it is destroyed. The amount of ozone in the atmosphere remained constant for centuries. However, humans have put chemicals into the air that break ozone down more rapidly than nature does. These chemicals are responsible for creating the "ozone hole" found over Antarctica each winter. This hole, shown in Figure 57b, has scientists worried.

ozone hole

Antarctica

ozone hole map

Figure 57b

The chemicals that are destroying the ozone are called *fluorocarbons* and are used in refrigerators and air conditioners. Chemicals released in the burning of fuels, such as nitrogen and sulfur oxides, also contribute. These chemicals become *catalysts*. A catalyst helps a chemical reaction occur but is not actually a part of the reaction. This means a catalyst is not used up in the reaction, and thus can cause more than one chemical reaction.

The fluorocarbons from refrigerators are inert (meaning they don't react easily) at the surface of the earth. However, over a period of a decade or more, they rise into the upper atmosphere where the ozone is. There, ultraviolet radiation breaks the fluorocarbons apart. These parts react with the ozone as a catalyst and destroy it.

How Everyday Things Work

Other chemicals can also destroy ozone. Nitrogen and sulfur oxides can act as catalysts to break down ozone when they are in the upper atmosphere. The combination of fluorocarbons and oxides breaks down more ozone than is made. Less ozone means less ultraviolet radiation is absorbed which means more gets through to damage the cells of living things on earth.

Although ozone is needed high in the atmosphere, it damages living tissue at the surface of the earth. Ozone is part of smog. The chemicals in polluted air are changed in sunlight to produce ozone. Because ozone reacts strongly with living tissue, people are urged not to exercise outside when ozone levels are high. The ozone literally breaks cells apart. Because you breathe more deeply when you exercise, you can do more damage to your lungs. The lung tissue is very sensitive to ozone and it is exposed to more ozone during exercise than when you are resting.

People often wonder if the ozone could be moved from the earth's surface to the upper atmosphere to protect us from ultraviolet rays. Unfortunately, this is not possible. The ozone at the surface of the earth is not concentrated and is therefore difficult to move. Also, huge amounts of ozone would need to be moved and would require a great deal of energy.

Methods are being used to protect the ozone where it is wanted and get rid of it where it is not. Nations all over the world have agreed to limit fluorocarbon production. Fluorocarbons are also being reclaimed from refrigerators and air conditioners, especially in cars, with what are called "vampire" systems, as shown in Figure 57c. Instead of letting the gases escape, they are collected and used again. Other forms of pollution are being reduced, so fewer nitric and sulfur oxides reach the upper atmosphere and less ozone is produced at ground level.

old fluorocarbons

Figure 57c

collecting tank

Review Questions

1) Where is ozone good and where is it bad? Why is this so?

2) How is ozone destroyed in the upper atmoshpere?

3) Why is ozone dangerous to breathe?

4) What is being done to save ozone where it is needed and reduce it where it is not desirable?

TEACHER

Answers

1) Ozone is good in the upper atmosphere where it absorbs ultraviolet radiation and bad at ground level where it harms living cells.

2) Ozone is destroyed catalytically in the upper atmosphere by fluorocarbons or by oxides of nitrogen and sulfur.

3) Ozone is very reactive and destroys cells. You should avoid strenuous exercise when ozone levels are high because it's harmful to your lungs.

4) Pollution control is helping to save ozone in the atmosphere and reduce it at ground level. Steps are being taken around the world to reduce the amount of damaging fluorocarbons produced and also to prevent their release into the air.

This idea of ozone being good in one place and bad in another may confuse students. You should carefully explain the problem and what causes it. The first data to show that ozone was being decreased in the upper atmosphere came around 1980 with the demonstration that an ozone hole was forming over Antarctica. This increased the amount of research on the subject and now scientists have developed a pretty good model for how the depletion occurs. The best conditions for destroying ozone occur at high altitude in very cold clouds. These clouds produce the best environment in which the catalytic destruction of ozone can occur. These conditions occur only during the Antarctic winter. The Arctic winter does not have conditions as favorable for the catalytic reactions because it is not quite as cold, so there does not seem to be a comparable ozone hole over the Arctic.

Artificially injecting ozone into the upper atmosphere does not seem to be the answer, as the energy requirements to do this are more than the total energy used by the U.S. during a year. Therefore, the ozone-destroying chemicals must be reduced. The problem is that these chemicals are long-lived. The ones released from an old refrigerator or car air-conditioning system will not rise to the upper atmosphere to do their damage for a decade or more. The fluorocarbon gas in air conditioners currently in use will eventually get into the atmosphere, but there are attempts now being made to collect these gases with "vampire" machines. Because fluorocarbons are being phased out of production and their replacements are not as good for refrigeration, sucking these gases out of old systems and putting them into new ones reduces the need for more fluorocarbons.

Ozone is the chemical in smog most harmful to living organisms. It can be reduced by producing cleaner burning engines and by reducing the amount of hydrocarbons and fluorocarbons released into the air.

58

Hazardous Waste Dumps

Hazardous waste must be kept out of the environment. Some chemicals or substances must literally be kept separate forever because they can kill or harm people, plants, and animals. The hazardous substances are toxic. So how do you keep these wastes separate for a very long time? This question has no easy answer.

If you dump a can of paint on the ground, some of it evaporates from the surface and some of it sinks into the ground. Chemicals in the paint may be toxic to plants and animals in the ground, and they may die as a result. Eventually, the chemicals in the paint may get into what is called the *water table*. The water table is the layer of saturated ground. This water eventually flows down hills. It is a slow process, but this flow of water keeps streams flowing even after it hasn't rained for a very long time. If the paint's chemicals get into the water table, they can travel long distances underground and pollute streams or wells.

There are many different kinds of hazardous wastes, but the worst are the ones that stay toxic for long periods of time. These wastes must be kept in toxic waste dumps and prevented from getting into the water table below the dump. How can this be done? Basically, a waterproof layer is placed under the dump. If water can't go down, then you prevent it from going into the water table.

So how do you make a waterproof layer under a hazardous waste dump? The process is a bit complex because many of the hazardous wastes are chemicals that can destroy the lining of the dump. A rubber lining would react with acids, oils, and other chemicals and would quickly be destroyed. The bottom would no longer be waterproof and the wastes would enter the groundwater.

One method for sealing the bottom of a hazardous waste dump is to start by digging a large hole in the ground. The hole is then lined with clay. Clay is used because it has very fine particles that are stuck together. Clay is a good substance to start with, because water normally cannot pass through it. Then, a layer of plastic is put down and made watertight. Next, a layer of material is added to protect the plastic layer from being torn when containers are dumped in, causing leaks.

Creating a container for hazardous waste, however, is not quite as simple as digging and lining a hole. When it rains, the rain fills up the hole because it can't drain out the bottom. Therefore, a pump system has to be built to remove the rainwater. This rainwater contains some hazardous wastes, so a machine must also purify the water.

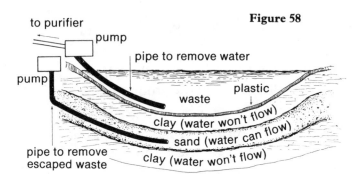

Figure 58

to purifier
pump
pipe to remove water
pump
waste
plastic
clay (water won't flow)
sand (water can flow)
pipe to remove escaped waste
clay (water won't flow)

This kind of dump works well for a period of time, but eventually the liner will leak. But how do you know when a leak occurs? In order to check for leaks, pipes go under the hole and are attached to pumps. If any waste leaks out, it enters the pipes and is pumped out. Often, there is a layer of clay and a layer of sand beneath the lined container. The layer of sand allows water and wastes to flow in it to the pipes. The bottom layers of clay and sand are there only if there is a leak. If there is a leak, pipes can pump the waste out until the leak can be fixed or the whole dump is cleaned out by moving the waste to another site.

Quite obviously, hazardous waste dumps are expensive to build. This is why we must try to avoid producing the wastes in the first place. Often manufacturers can use different manufacturing processes that produce less waste. School science classes are starting to use "micro-chemistry," meaning that they use much smaller test tubes than the ones you are used to seeing. If smaller amounts of chemicals are used in the labs, less chemical waste is created. People are finding that because the cost of getting rid of waste is high, it pays to produce less waste.

Review Questions

1) What happens to chemicals poured on the ground?

2) What happens if chemicals get into the water table?

3) How is a hazardous waste dump constructed?

4) How is it determined if a hazardous waste dump is working properly?

5) What may cause people to make less waste that is hazardous?

TEACHER

Answers

1) Some of the chemicals evaporate, while others enter the ground and kill organisms.

2) Chemicals in the water table flow with the water and eventually pollute streams and wells. Removing such contaminants from the ground is always expensive.

3) Generally clay is used as the bottom layer and then other impermeable layers are put in place. Pipes run under the site to check for leaks if they occur. Pumps are needed to remove rainwater and machinery is needed to purify the water that is pumped out.

4) Pipes running under the dump are pumped to see if chemicals are leaking out.

5) Industry and individuals can work toward creating less hazardous waste, and individuals can be more careful in what materials they purchase. School labs can use smaller amounts of chemicals.

One of the purposes of this section is to make students aware of the difficulties we face when dealing with hazardous wastes. The Love Canal situation, where the Hooker Chemical Company simply buried their wastes, illustrates the need for a different solution to the hazardous waste problem. After a number of years, houses were built on this waste dump by people unaware of the chemicals buried in the ground. The chemicals oozed up out of the ground and poisoned people. Students should also realize, however, that there is no simple solution to the hazardous waste problem.

The technology for hazardous waste disposal is expensive. Many wastes stay toxic for extremely long periods of time. The description of a hazardous waste dump in this section is only one of many designs, but they all strive to achieve the same end—to contain the waste so that it can't escape.

One of the problems with the dump discussed here is that it must literally be maintained forever. This is expensive and if a leak ever forms, then the whole toxic dump must be moved before repairs can be made.

An idea for a class discussion might be whether burning some of these toxic wastes might be helpful. If they can be burned into nontoxic products and no toxic smoke is released, then you get rid of the wastes rather than having to keep them forever. The problem with this method is that it is hard to burn the wastes cleanly, so the equipment is expensive to build and operate. Also, people don't like the idea of having a hazardous waste incinerator near them. However, this method is used in Europe and might be a possible alternative to waste disposal here in the U.S.

Another method for dealing with hazardous waste is to recycle as much of it as is possible. Many of the chemicals can be used in industry, but they are impure. Methods are being used to recycle some chemicals, but that is also a difficult process.

59

How Nuclear Power Plants Generate Electricity

A nuclear power plant generates electricity by having steam go through turbines that turn generators. This is similar to how coal-fired plants generate electricity. The difference between a nuclear power station and a coal-fired station is that the steam is produced by nuclear energy rather than by the chemical energy stored in coal.

Nuclear power plants use *fission,* the breaking apart of atomic nuclei, to heat the water. Fission occurs when a large atomic nucleus, such as uranium, is broken into two smaller parts. Fission releases energy which is used to boil the water for making steam.

Fission breaks apart the nucleus of the atom, which is made up of positively charged protons and neutral neutrons. Negative electrons form a cloud around the nucleus. Although the nucleus is very small, it contains more than 99.9% of all the atom's mass. If the nucleus were the size of a pea and placed at home plate of a baseball field, the electrons would be in the outfield. This shows how small the nucleus is compared to the entire atom.

Fission starts when a neutron enters the nucleus of a uranium atom. This makes the normally stable nucleus unstable. The nucleus breaks into two nearly equal pieces, plus some neutrons. These neutrons can enter other uranium nuclei and cause them to

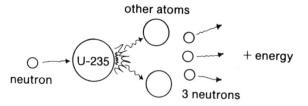

Figure 59a

fission, as shown in Figure 59a. The control rods in the reactor absorb neutrons, so that only one neutron from each fission hits another atom. The neutron that hits another atom causes that atom to fission. That atom releases neutrons, so it can cause another atom to fission. This is called a "chain reaction" and works in much the same way that one domino in a line can knock down another domino. Once it gets started, it keeps going.

How Everyday Things Work

Control rods absorb neutrons. To gain more power from the reactor, the control rods are pulled out a little so fewer neutrons are absorbed and more escape to cause fission. To stop the reaction, the control rods are put into the reactor and they absorb all the neutrons. With no neutrons entering nuclei, no fission occurs.

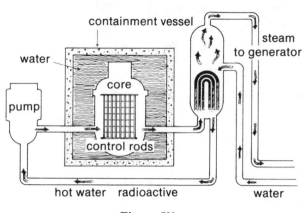

Figure 59b

The fission process heats the water in the reactor core and generates steam. Generally, the water circulating in the reactor is kept separate from the water that goes through the turbines, because it becomes radioactive. A heat exchanger transfers heat from the water circulating through the reactor to the water that drives the turbines, as shown in Figure 59b.

Nuclear power plants are more dangerous to operate than coal-fired power plants, although the coal-fired plants release carbon dioxide that can cause global warming. The reason is that the atoms formed in the fission process are radioactive. If those radioactive atoms get out of the reactor, all living organisms suffer. This happened at Chernobyl, Russia in 1986. The nuclear reactor was not operated properly and the reactor exploded, releasing huge quantities of radioactive atoms. Many people died and many have continued to suffer from radiation effects. The radiation can cause mutations or kill cells. If enough cells are killed, the person dies.

The nuclear power plant at Chernobyl was not built in the same way as are the ones in the United States and Europe. It lacked what is called a *containment vessel,* which is designed to hold the radioactive materials inside in case of an accident. The design of the Chernobyl reactor was also much more dangerous. The combination of a less-safe design with improper operation led to the disaster. Properly built and run reactors should be safe. The reactor operators at Chernobyl neglected all safety precautions and the world has paid for it.

One problem that all nuclear reactors have, however, is that they produce radioactive waste. This waste stays radioactive for long periods of time and cannot be made nonradioactive. The problem then is where to store it. This is a problem with no easy solution and will be covered in the next chapter.

Review Questions

1) How is a nuclear power plant different from a coal-fired plant?

2) What happens in a nuclear chain reaction?

3) What do the control rods do and how can they stop a nuclear reaction?

4) What caused the Chernobyl accident?

5) What are the main problems with nuclear power plants?

TEACHER

Answers

1) Nuclear reactors use fission of atomic nuclei rather than chemical energy to make steam to run turbines.

2) One atom fissions and a neutron from that fission causes the next atom to fission, which releases another neutron, etc.

3) Control rods absorb neutrons. In normal operation, they are placed so they absorb all but one neutron from each fission. To shut the reactor down, they are moved farther into the reactor and they absorb all neutrons. No neutrons, no fission.

4) The accident at Chernobyl was caused by a poorly designed reactor and improper operation. In order to run an experiment, the operators had turned off all the safety features that could have saved the reactor.

5) Nuclear power plants have to be run safely because accidents can release dangerous amounts of radioactive materials. They also produce radioactive waste, which still cannot be disposed of in a safe manner.

Nuclear power is something that all students will have to make decisions about. They should have some awareness of how reactors produce energy in order to make educated decisions about them. This section tries to explain how nuclear reactors work.

If nuclear reactors are built and run properly, they present little risk to the environment. Virtually all major incidents and accidents at nuclear power stations have been caused by neglect of proper procedures or construction methods. Just as you are careful in building and flying an airplane, you must be careful in building and running a nuclear plant. The plant at Chernobyl had a poor design and the operators were flagrantly violating safety procedure. They were also ignorant of the nuclear physics involved and did not completely understand what could happen and why. So we do need to ask if it is *possible* to be sure that *all* reactors can be run safely.

The student discussion of how the plants run is abbreviated. The uranium fuel is generally made of slightly enriched uranium. One isotope of uranium, uranium-235, fissions easily, but it makes up about only .5% of all the uranium found in nature. The rest is uranium-238. Power plants typically use enriched uranium that is 3 to 4% uranium-235. This allows the fission reaction to proceed more easily. Uranium-238 does not fission, although it can be changed to plutonium-239 after absorbing a neutron. Plutonium-239 will fission. Neutrons released in fission have too much energy to cause fissions efficiently and are called "fast neutrons." A moderator such as water can make them "slow neutrons," which can cause fission. This why water is very useful as a coolant in power plants.

The operation of the plant requires that new fuel be put in on a yearly basis. Normal maintenance is done on the reactor during the refueling. The spent fuel is removed to storage ponds where it is kept until it is taken to a permanent storage area. The problems associated with radioactive waste are outlined in the next section.

60

Radioactive Waste

Radioactive waste is different from other kinds of waste in that it emits particles. Most hazardous waste is dangerous if you inhale it, drink it, or get it on your skin. Radioactive waste is dangerous if you get near it. It is worse if it gets on your skin or inside you, but you can suffer damage without even touching it.

Radioactive waste is also more permanent than nonradioactive waste. Many hazardous wastes can be burned, neutralized, or recycled. This reduces the amount of hazardous waste. However, it is not possible to change radioactive waste into nonradioactive waste by any economical means.

Radioactive substances give off one or more of the three radioactive particles: alpha, beta, and gamma. These particles are called *radiation* and are given off from the decaying nuclei of atoms. Radioactive atoms stay radioactive until they release their radiation, even though they may undergo chemical changes, such as burning. When the chemical changes occur, the radioactive atom is found in a different chemical.

Radiation causes damage because the particles can kill or damage cells. Alpha, beta, and gamma particles have large amounts of energy. When they strike a cell, they can knock atoms from their normal positions. Cells can be killed if the wrong atoms are knocked out of place, especially if the damage affects the DNA. If the DNA is broken or modified, it no longer gives the right instructions to the cell. The cell stops functioning properly and may die or become cancerous. Radioactive substances are dangerous, especially if they get inside you, because your body will absorb all the radiation.

If radioactive waste is so dangerous, what can be done with it? Radioactive substances do become less radioactive as time goes by. They have what is called a "half-life." In one half-life, an object loses half its radioactivity. In the next half-life, it loses half of the remaining radioactivity, so that after the second half-life it would have ¼ the initial radioactivity (½ × ½ = ¼). This is shown in Figure 60a. Radioactive materials do become less dangerous over time.

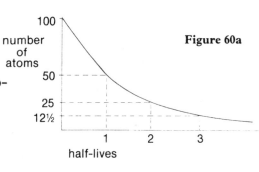

Figure 60a

But how dangerous are radioactive wastes? *Low-level* radioactive wastes are not very dangerous. These are wastes from medical procedures, industrial processes, and the clothing of people who work in nuclear power plants. The radiation is generally of short half-life, meaning that it quickly becomes only slightly radioactive. Also, the amount of radiation given off by a pile of clothes is minimal. True, you would not want it in your living room, but it is easy to store this kind of material safely. Some towns and cities are actively seeking to have this kind of waste dump within their boundaries because there is little danger. They make money from taxing the waste site and are at little or no risk.

Medium-level radioactive waste is more dangerous and must be kept in places with more careful safeguards. Generally, this type of material also has a relatively short half-life so it, too, becomes safer quite quickly.

The most dangerous kind of waste is the *high-level* radioactive waste. This type of waste is produced by nuclear power plants or in the production of atomic weapons. It produces large amounts of radioactivity and is long-lived. Plutonium is one kind of dangerous waste and has a half-life of 24,000 years. That is a long time to wait for it to become half as radioactive. There are still no permanent storage sites in the United States for this kind of waste, so it is stored in temporary containers. These containers have sometimes leaked and allowed the radioactive materials to get into the environment. Because the radioactivity is so long-lived, spills like this will be a problem for future generations.

Review Questions

1) Why is radioactive waste different from other waste?

2) What makes radioactive waste dangerous to be around?

3) What is given off as an atom decays and what damage can it cause?

4) Why is low-level waste safer than high-level waste?

5) How is high-level waste presently being stored?

TEACHER

Answers

1) Radioactive waste is dangerous because it cannot be changed into nonradioactive waste. Only with time does it lose its radioactivity, and with some waste, this takes a **long** time.

2) The alpha, beta, and gamma rays can enter your body.

3) The radiation causes damage to cells, perhaps killing them or even causing a cancer to start.

4) Low-level waste is only slightly radioactive and generally has a short half-life. High-level waste is very radioactive and has long half-lives.

5) Presently, high-level waste is being stored in temporary containers.

Knowing about radioactive waste is important for students. They will have to make decisions about what to do with it in the future. In order to make rational decisions, they must know about radioactivity. This section shows that there is a difference between normal hazardous waste and radioactive waste. The difference is important.

An attempt has been made to make this section factual and not one-sided. However, some people will be opposed to the way that "low-level" waste is discussed, saying that it is much more dangerous than described. Others will say that the high-level waste is more or less dangerous than implied in this section. However, this is a starting point for the discussion and gives the students some facts.

In order to understand radioactivity, students must know about radiation and about half-lives. They must also understand that it is not possible to change the radioactivity of an atom by any practical means. The nucleus of the atom is difficult to change and most changes simply make it more radioactive. (This happens to the pipes of nuclear reactors. The steel absorbs radiation and becomes radioactive steel.)

The idea of half-life is also important. Short-lived radioactive substances are relatively safe. Such substances are used in medical tests and treatments. The substances can be traced in the body because they are radioactive, but the substances are chosen so that they very quickly lose their radioactivity. The problem with most nuclear waste from power plants is that its half-life is long.

Presently, a permanent site for storage of high-level waste is being considered in Nevada. The plan is to concentrate the waste, then mold it in a glass or ceramic form that is impervious to corrosion and water. It will then be placed in a storage area where water will not seep. Hopefully, the system can be started soon because there is lots of waste in temporary storage in or near nuclear reactors. Some of the containers are getting old and some have actually leaked.

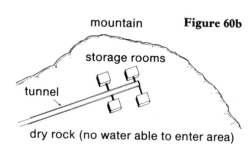

mountain   **Figure 60b**

storage rooms

tunnel

dry rock (no water able to enter area)

Index

S